LEVEL

4

motivation
MATH

TEKS–Based Alignment to STAAR®

student edition

Critical Thinking for Life!
Mentoring Minds

Publisher
Michael L. Lujan, M.Ed.

Editorial Director
Teresa Sherman, B.S.E.

Production Coordinator
Kim Barnes, B.B.A.

Digital Production Artists
Sarah Poff, B.S.
Ashley Francis, A.A.

Illustrators
Judy Bankhead, M.F.A.
Gabriel Urbina, A.A.S.

Content Development Team
Marian Rainwater, M.Ed.
Karen White, M.Ed.
Stephanie Christian, M.Ed.
Jackie Cannon, M.Ed.
Karen Gardiner, B.S.I.S.
Jan Hood, M.Ed.
Lori Roper, B.S.E.
Laura Young, B.S.E.
Brooke North, B.A.

Content Editorial Team
Allison Wiley, B.S.E.
Marian Rainwater, M.Ed.
Karen White, M.Ed.
Stephanie Christian, M.Ed.
Karen Reeves, M.Ed.
Jennifer Mallios, B.A.
Heather Zisler, B.S.I.S.
Cathy Cutler, B.S.E.

Critical Thinking for Life!™
Mentoring Minds

PO Box 8843 · Tyler, TX 75711

[p] 800.585.5258 · [f] 800.838.8186

For other great products from Mentoring Minds,
please visit our website at:
mentoring**minds**.com

ISBN: 978-1-938935-65-7

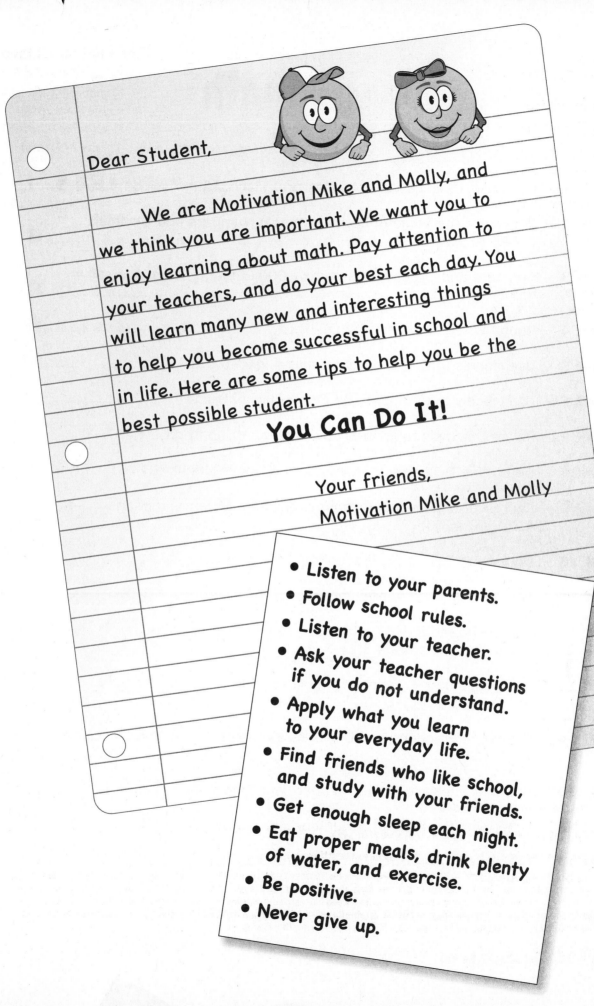

Dear Student,

We are Motivation Mike and Molly, and we think you are important. We want you to enjoy learning about math. Pay attention to your teachers, and do your best each day. You will learn many new and interesting things to help you become successful in school and in life. Here are some tips to help you be the best possible student.

You Can Do It!

Your friends,
Motivation Mike and Molly

- Listen to your parents.
- Follow school rules.
- Listen to your teacher.
- Ask your teacher questions if you do not understand.
- Apply what you learn to your everyday life.
- Find friends who like school, and study with your friends.
- Get enough sleep each night.
- Eat proper meals, drink plenty of water, and exercise.
- Be positive.
- Never give up.

motivation**math**™

Table of Contents

1 Choose one digit between 1 and 9. Write the same digit in each place in the place value chart below.

	,			
thousands	**,**	hundreds	tens	ones

How does the value of the digit in the thousands place compare to the value of the digit in the hundreds place?

Answer: _____

_____

How does the value of the digit in the ones place compare to the value of the digit in the tens place?

Answer: _____

_____

2 Fill in the blanks.

The digit 4 in 49,308 has a value _____ times as much as the 4 in 4,061.

The 6 in the number 648 has a value _____ as much as the 6 in the number 6,140.

3 The teacher asks Mel and Kate to use base 10 blocks to model the number that is ten times the value of 4 rods. Mel's model uses 4 unit cubes. Kate's model uses 4 flats. Which girl is correct?

Answer: _____

Explain your answer.

_____

_____

4 Write a sentence that compares the values of the nines in the number 69.92.

Answer: _____

_____

5 Look at these numbers.

0.31   0.13

Which number has a 3 with a value $\frac{1}{10}$ the value of the 3 in 3.01?

Answer: _____

Which number has a 1 with a value 10 times the value of 1 in 3.01?

Answer: _____

6 In the number 8.88, how is the value of the underlined digit related to the digits on its left and right?

Answer: _____

_____

7 Fill in the blanks.

The digit 7 in 0.37 has a value _____ the value of the 7 in 0.73.

The 1 in 425.1 has a value _____ times the value of the 1 in 7.51.

8 Armand ran the 100-yard dash in 17.18 seconds. Arturo's time has an 8 with a value 10 times the value of the 8 in Armand's time. What could be Arturo's time on the 100-yard dash?

Answer: _____

1 The baseball stadium in Cleveland, Ohio, holds 42,000 people. The number for Saturday's attendance contains a 4 with a value $\frac{1}{10}$ the value of the 4 in 42,000. Which could be Saturday's attendance?

Ⓐ 402,510   Ⓒ 25,420

Ⓑ 34,612   Ⓓ 40,965

2 The average distance from the Sun to Venus is 67,237,910 miles. The average distance from the Sun to Earth is 92,955,807 miles. Which statement is true?

Ⓕ The value of 2 in Venus' distance is 10 times the value of 2 in Earth's distance.

Ⓖ The value of 2 in Earth's distance is $\frac{1}{10}$ the value of 2 in Venus' distance.

Ⓗ The value of 2 in Venus' distance is $\frac{1}{10}$ the value of 2 in Earth's distance.

Ⓙ The value of 2 in the two distances is equal.

3 In the number 555.5$\underline{5}$, each digit is a 5, but the value of each 5 is different based on its place in the number. How does the value of the 5 in the tenths place compare to the value of the underlined digit 5?

Ⓐ They have the same value.

Ⓑ The value of 5 in the tenths place is 10 times as much.

Ⓒ The value of 5 in the tenths place is $\frac{1}{10}$ as much.

Ⓓ The value of 5 in the tenths place is 100 times as much.

4 Mr. Chang's students planted bean seeds and compared the growth after three weeks. The chart shows the heights of the plants in centimeters.

Plant	Height (cm)
A	36.7
B	34.9
C	38.4
D	43.6

How does the 4 in Plant B's height compare to the 4 in Plant C's height?

Ⓕ The value of 4 in Plant B's height is the same as the 4 in Plant C's height.

Ⓖ The value of 4 in Plant C's height is 10 times the value of the 4 in Plant B's height.

Ⓗ The value of 4 in Plant B's height is $\frac{1}{10}$ the value of the 4 in Plant C's height.

Ⓙ The value of 4 in Plant B's height is 10 times the value of the 4 in Plant C's height.

5 Kevin has $1,427 in a savings account. His brother, Harley, has saved an amount with a 4 that is $\frac{1}{10}$ the value of the 4 in Kevin's savings account. How much could Harley have in his savings account?

Ⓐ $114   Ⓒ $1,245

Ⓑ $408   Ⓓ $4,300

1 The school band sold 3,305 raffle tickets to raise money for a trip to Disney World®. Which equation shows the relationship between the threes in the number of tickets sold?

Ⓐ $3 \times 1 = 3$

Ⓑ $30 \div 1 = 30$

Ⓒ $300 \div 10 = 30$

Ⓓ $300 \times 10 = 3,000$

2 The table shows the scores for the top 4 players in a video game contest.

Player	Score
Albert	401,987
Destiny	359,847
José	321,795
Simar	297,634

Which player's score contains a 9 with a value 10 times the value of the 9 in Destiny's score?

Ⓕ Albert   Ⓗ Simar

Ⓖ José   Ⓙ Not here

3 A large flat screen television costs $2,109. A smaller television is priced at $1,987. Which statement shows how the value of the 1 in the first price is related to the value of the 1 in the second price?

Ⓐ It represents the same value.

Ⓑ It represents 10 times the value.

Ⓒ It represents $\frac{1}{10}$ the value.

Ⓓ It represents 100 times the value.

4 The table shows the discounts for differently priced toys at a toy store.

Original Price ($)	Discount ($)
$15.90	$1.59
$24.60	$2.46
$49.90	$4.99

What is the relationship between the values of the digits in the two amounts?

Ⓕ The digits in each original price are 10 times the values of the same digits in the discount.

Ⓖ The digits in each discount are 10 times the values of the same digits in the original price.

Ⓗ The values of the digits in the original prices and the discounts are equal.

Ⓙ The digits in each original price are $\frac{1}{10}$ the values of the same digits in the discount.

5 Which statement correctly compares the values of the shaded areas in Figures A and B?

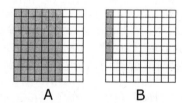

A   B

Ⓐ Figure A has a value that is $\frac{1}{10}$ as much as Figure B.

Ⓑ Figure A has a value that is 10 times as much as Figure B.

Ⓒ Figure A has a value that is 100 times as much as Figure B.

Ⓓ Figure A has a value that is 7 times as much as Figure B.

1 How does the 4 in the number 4,326 compare to the 4 in the number 324,765?

Ⓐ Both represent the same value.

Ⓑ Both represent 4 ten thousands.

Ⓒ The value of the 4 in 4,326 is $\frac{1}{10}$ the value of the 4 in 324,765.

Ⓓ The value of the 4 in 4,326 is 10 times the value of the 4 in 324,765.

2 The fourth-grade classes at Eastside Elementary School had a read-a-thon. The students read a total of 29,884 minutes. How do the values of the digit 8 compare in this number?

Ⓕ The 8 in the hundreds place is 100 times as much as the 8 in the tens place.

Ⓖ The 8 in the tens place is 10 times as much as the 8 in the hundreds place.

Ⓗ The 8 in the tens place is $\frac{1}{10}$ the value of the 8 in the hundreds place.

Ⓙ The 8 in the tens place is equal in value to the 8 in the hundreds place.

3 The digit 9 appears twice in the number 9,940,317. Which equation correctly compares the values of each digit 9 in this number?

Ⓐ 9,000,000 ÷ 9,000,000 = 1

Ⓑ 9 × 9,000,000 = 81,000,000

Ⓒ 9,000,000 × 10 = 90,000,000

Ⓓ 9,000,000 ÷ 10 = 900,000

4 How does the value of 2 dimes compare to the value of 2 dollars?

Ⓕ The value of 2 dimes is 10 times as much as the value of 2 dollars.

Ⓖ The value of 2 dimes is 20 times as much as the value of 2 dollars.

Ⓗ The value of 2 dimes is $\frac{1}{10}$ as much as the value of 2 dollars.

Ⓙ The value of 2 dimes is $\frac{1}{20}$ as much as the value of 2 dollars.

5 In 2013, the total rainfall in Carey's hometown was 26.34 inches. He made this table to show the yearly rainfall in his hometown for the four preceding years.

Year	Rainfall (in.)
2012	25.13
2011	23.90
2010	28.32
2009	30.08

In which year did the total rainfall in Carey's hometown contain a 3 with 10 times the value of the 3 in the total rainfall for 2013?

Ⓐ 2012   Ⓒ 2010

Ⓑ 2011   Ⓓ 2009

6 Shawna has $435.15 in her savings account. Which of these numbers has a 1 with a value that is $\frac{1}{10}$ the value of the 1 in $435.15?

Ⓕ $451.89   Ⓗ $360.71

Ⓖ $215.75   Ⓙ $199.50

1   Complete the place value chart to show the value represented by each digit in the number 333,333.

Hundred Thousands	Ten Thousands	Thousands	Hundreds	Tens	Ones
3	3	3	3	3	3
The value of this 3 is _____.	The value of this 3 is _____.	The value of this 3 is _____.	The value of this 3 is _____.	The value of this 3 is _____.	The value of this 3 is _____.

What is the relationship between the 3 in the ten thousands place and the 3 in the thousands place?

Answer: _____

_____

What is the relationship between the 3 in the ones place and the 3 in the hundreds place?

Answer: _____

_____

Write a statement that is true about the place value chart.

_____

2   Joshua plays a game using these number tiles.

In order from greatest to least, write the 3 largest possible numbers Joshua could create with the number tiles if he uses each tile only one time in each number.

_____   _____   _____

Write a statement that compares the values of the digit 5 in the first and third numbers.

Answer: _____

Unit 1 Journal/Vocabulary Activity

Journal

Analysis
i
Analyze

Sandra wants to trick her brother. She says, "I know a digit with a value that stays the same no matter what place it appears in the number."

What digit does Sandra mean? _____

Explain your answer. _____

_____

_____

Vocabulary Activity

Play tic-tac-toe with a partner. Pairs use one tic-tac-toe board. Together, partners select and record 9 vocabulary words in the spaces on the tic-tac-toe board. Decide which player is X and which player is O. Player X begins by choosing a space and providing the definition of the word. If correct, the player marks an X in the space. Play passes to player O who repeats the process. The first player to mark three spaces in a row, column, or diagonal wins.

Words

billions
decimal point
digit
hundreds
hundredths
millions
ones
place value
tens
tenths
thousands
value

 motivation**math**™LEVEL 4 ©2014 mentoring**minds**.com

Motivation Mike says, "I wish I could shake your hand!"

It's a Mystery to Me!

Use these clues to find the mystery number.

- The number has 9 digits.

- The digit in the tenths place is the digit used to represent a half dozen.

- The digit in the tens place is the value of a fraction with the same numerator and denominator.

- The value of one of the digits is 40,000.

- The value of the digit in the ones place is 10 times the value of the digit in the tenths place.

- The digit in the hundreds place is the sum of the two digits to its right.

- The digit in the thousands place is half the digit in the ten thousands place.

- The digit in the millions place is equal to the number of pints in four quarts.

- The digit in the hundred thousands place has a value one-tenth the value of the digit in the millions place.

- The digit in the ten millions place is the difference between the digit in the hundreds place and the digit in the thousands place.

What is the mystery number? Place a decimal point to separate the whole number place values from the decimal place values.

_____ _____ _____ _____ _____ _____ _____ _____ _____

Put commas in the number to mark the place value periods.

Write this number in word form. _____

_____

_____

1 Jack looked at the place values in Pattern A and Pattern B.

Pattern A: 2, 20, 200, 2,000, 20,000

Pattern B: 40,000, 4,000, 400, 40, 4

What rule should Jack find for each pattern?

Answer: _____

_____

_____

_____

2 Last summer, Jon earned $916 mowing lawns. His brother, Gabe, earned $791 completing chores in the neighborhood. Compare the value of the 9 in each of the two numbers. How do the values compare?

Answer: _____

_____

_____

3 At the track meet, Ervin won the 100-meter dash with a time of 12.45 seconds. Landon finished second. Landon's time contains a 4 with a value $\frac{1}{10}$ the value of the 4 in Ervin's time. What could be Landon's time in the 100-meter dash?

Answer: _____

4 Shade each model to show a decimal number so that the number shaded on Figure A has a value that is 10 times as much as the number shaded on Figure B.

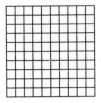

Figure A   Figure B

5 Trisha compares the values of the digits in two decimal numbers.

0.65   0.56

What can Trisha say about the values of the digits?

_____

_____

_____

✂ -

Parent Activities

1. Create numbers to the billions place in which at least one digit is repeated in two adjacent places (e.g., 456,778). Discuss the relationship between the repeated digits (e.g., The value of the 7 in the hundreds place is 10 times the value of the 7 in the tens place.).

2. Compare the values of the same digit in money amounts. Use dimes and pennies to create 44¢. Ask your child how the value of 4 pennies compares to the value of 4 dimes (e.g., 4 pennies is $\frac{1}{10}$ the value of 4 dimes).

1 Evan purchased stickers for a school project. On Saturday, he bought 8 packs of 10 stickers, 4 packs of 100 stickers, and 54 single stickers. On Sunday he saw an ad at a local hobby shop for stickers on sale at half price. He purchased 6 packs of 1,000. How many stickers did Evan purchase? Write an equation to show your answer.

Answer: $10 \times 8 = 80$ $4 \times 100 =$
400 $6,000$ $54 +$

$6,534$

2 Geographers estimate that the approximate land area of Earth, in square kilometers, is 1 hundred million + 4 ten millions + 8 millions + 8 hundred thousands + 4 ten thousands + 7 thousands + 7 hundreds + 5 tens. How is this number written in standard form?

Answer: $148,847,750$

3 Adam and Jacob used base 10 blocks to model whole numbers. Adam used 7 large cubes, 3 flats, 24 rods, and 6 units. Jacob used 5 large cubes, 22 flats, 14 rods, and 23 units. Which student modeled the larger number?

Answer: _____

Explain your answer.

_____

_____

_____

4 Devin writes a number that contains the digits 2, 4, 6, 7, 9, and 0. The 0 is in the tens place, and the 7 is in the hundredths place. What is the largest number Devin could have written?

Answer: _____

Write the number in expanded notation.

_____

_____

What is the value of the 6 in your number?

Answer: _____

What is the value of the 4 in your number?

Answer: _____

What is the value of the 7 in your number?

Answer: _____

5 Maggie's mom went grocery shopping. The receipt shows the items she bought. Use expanded notation to write the total amount Maggie's mom spent.

Fiedler's FoodMart 1327 Franklin Ave. Oakdale, TX 73737	
Lunchable	2.69
Hot dogs	2.79
Paper plates	3.47
Soda-24 pk	4.06
Subtotal	13.01
TAX	0.28
Total	$13.29

Answer: _____

_____

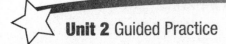

1 Nancy correctly writes the number 278,932 in three different ways. Which is **NOT** a way to write 278,932?

Ⓐ 200,000 + 70,000 + 8,000 + 900 + 30 + 2

Ⓑ 2 hundred thousands + 6 ten thousands + 18 thousands + 7 hundreds + 23 tens + 2 ones

Ⓒ 200,000 + 60,000 + 18,000 + 900 + 20 + 12

Ⓓ 2 + 70 + 800 + 9,000 + 30,000 + 200,000

2 Nina thought of a mystery number. She wrote this clue to help her classmates determine the number.

The number has 7 ones, 9 hundreds, 3 hundred millions, 4 thousands, 9 hundred thousands, and 6 millions.

What is Nina's mystery number?

Ⓕ 793,496

Ⓖ 306,904,907

Ⓗ 369,497

Ⓙ 904,306,907

3 Caroline's mom spent $14.82 at the gas station. How should Caroline write this amount in expanded notation?

Ⓐ 10.0 + 4.0 + 8.0 + 2.0

Ⓑ 10 + 4 + 8.0 + 0.20

Ⓒ 10 + 4 + 0.8 + 0.02

Ⓓ Not here

Use the table to answer questions 4 and 5.

The table shows the populations of four Texas cities.

City	Population
Houston	2,160,821
Austin	842,592
Dallas	1,241,162
San Antonio	1,383,951

4 Which of the following correctly represents the population of Dallas in expanded notation?

Ⓕ 1,000,000 + 200,000 + 400,000 + 1,000 + 10 + 6 + 2

Ⓖ 1,000,000 + 200,000 + 40,000 + 1,000 + 100 + 60 + 2

Ⓗ 1,000,000 + 2,000,000 + 400,000 + 1,000 + 100 + 60 + 2

Ⓙ 100,000 + 200,000 + 40,000 + 1,000 + 100 + 60 + 2

5 Which city's population has an 8 with a value of 80,000 and a 9 with a value of 900?

Ⓐ Houston   Ⓒ Dallas

Ⓑ Austin   Ⓓ San Antonio

6 Bronson wrote a 6-digit number with a 6 in the ten thousands place, a 5 in the tens place, a 7 in the hundreds place, and a 2 in the thousands place. Which number could Bronson have written?

Ⓕ 62,751   Ⓗ 862,754

Ⓖ 657,200   Ⓙ 860,752

1 The Martin family traveled on Interstate Highway 10 across Texas from El Paso to the Louisiana border. They recorded a total distance of eight hundred ninety-five and six-tenths miles. How is this number written in numerals?

Ⓐ 80,095.6   Ⓒ 8,956

Ⓑ 895.6   Ⓓ 895.06

2 The results of the 100-meter men's butterfly swimming event in the 2012 Olympics are shown on the table.

100-Meter Men's Butterfly

Swimmer	Time (sec)
Nathan Adrian	47.52
James Magnussen	47.53
Brent Hayden	47.80
Yannick Agnel	47.84

Which swimmer's time can be written in expanded notation as shown below?

40 + 7 + 0.5 + 0.03

Ⓕ Nathan Adrian

Ⓖ James Magnussen

Ⓗ Brent Hayden

Ⓙ Yannick Agnel

3 Jolene's Jellybean Company sponsors a Guess My Number jellybean contest. Jolene pours twelve bags of 1,000 jellybeans into a large container. Then she adds 9 bags of 100 jellybeans. Finally she mixes in eighteen bags of 10 jellybeans. How many jellybeans are in Jolene's container?

Ⓐ 13,080   Ⓒ 12,180

Ⓑ 12,111   Ⓓ 12,918

Use the table to answer questions 4 and 5.

Mr. Miller's science class studied vertebrate animals. They made this table showing the number of species for each classification of vertebrates.

Class	Number of Species
Amphibians	7,191
Birds	9,998
Fish	31,384
Mammals	5,490
Reptiles	9,084

4 Which class of vertebrates has a 9 with a value of 9,000 and an 8 with a value of 80?

Ⓕ Birds   Ⓗ Mammals

Ⓖ Fish   Ⓙ Reptiles

5 Which of these is **NOT** a way to write the number of fish species?

Ⓐ 30,000 + 1,000 + 300 + 80 + 4

Ⓑ 2 ten thousands + 11 thousands + 3 hundreds + 5 tens + 34 ones

Ⓒ 30 ten thousands + 11 thousands + 3 hundreds + 80 tens + 4 ones

Ⓓ 30,000 + 1,300 + 84

6 Brandon wrote an 8-digit number. In expanded notation, the number is 700,000 + 3,000 + 900 + 10 + 1 + 0.08. How is Brandon's number written in standard form?

Ⓕ 703,911.8   Ⓗ 73,911.08

Ⓖ 730,911.08   Ⓙ 703,911.08

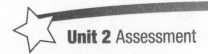

1   Liseth thinks of a mystery number. She writes 4 clues for the number.

   • The number contains 7 digits.
   • The number contains a 5 with a value of 5 hundredths.
   • The number contains a 2 with a value of 20,000.
   • The number contains 8 tens.

   Which could Liseth's number be?

   Ⓐ   7,328,510   Ⓒ   307,527.8

   Ⓑ   520,586.45   Ⓓ   24,083.15

2   Molly's teacher asked three students to write the number 56,017.83 in expanded notation.

   Dell: 56 thousands + 17 tens + 83 tenths

   Libby: 50,000 + 6,000 + 100 + 70 + 0.8 + 0.03

   Margo: 50 ten thousands + 6 thousands + 1 ten + 7 ones + 0.8 + 0.03

   Which students wrote correct answers?

   Ⓕ   All three students were correct.

   Ⓖ   Only Dell was correct.

   Ⓗ   Both Dell and Libby were correct.

   Ⓙ   None of the students were correct.

3   The New York City Public Library has 50,000,000 + 2,000,000 + 900,000 + 40,000 + 6,000 + 300 + 90 + 8 items in its collections. How is this number written in standard form?

   Ⓐ   502,946,398   Ⓒ   52,946,398

   Ⓑ   52,940,639.8   Ⓓ   5,294,639.8

Use the table to answer questions 4 and 5.

The Pacific Ocean has the deepest ocean trenches in the world. The table shows the depths, in feet, of 4 trenches.

Pacific Ocean Trenches

Name	Depth (ft)
Mariana Trench	35,797.6
Tonga Trench	35,702.1
Philippine Trench	34,461.9
Kuril Trench	34,586.6

4   Which ocean trench contains a 5 with a value of 5,000, a 7 with a value of 7 hundreds, and a 6 with a value of 0.6?

   Ⓕ   Mariana

   Ⓖ   Tonga

   Ⓗ   Philippine

   Ⓙ   Kuril

5   Which of these does **NOT** represent the depth of the Kuril Trench?

   Ⓐ   34 thousands + 5 hundreds + 8 tens + 6 ones + 6 tenths

   Ⓑ   30,000 + 4,000 + 500 + 80 + 6 + 0.6

   Ⓒ   30,000 + 4,000 + 400 + 160 + 61 + 0.6

   Ⓓ   20,000 + 14,000 + 500 + 50 + 36 + 0.6

Standard 4.2(B)–Readiness

Unit 2 Critical Thinking

1 Complete the chart. The first number has been completed as an example.

Number	How many millions?	How many hundred thousands?	How many ten thousands?	How many thousands?	How many hundreds?	How many tens?	How many ones?
3,538,497	3	5	3	7	14	9	7
4,034,921	4		2	14	8		1
679,205	0	5	17		0	20	5
8,915,224	7	19	1		12	2	4
653,007		5	15	0			7

2 Mrs. Martin, the school librarian, needs to record the titles of all the books in the library in folders on her computer. She must decide how many book titles to place in each folder. There are 57,000 books in the school library.

How many folders would Mrs. Martin need if she organizes the books in folders of 1,000?

Answer: _____

How many folders would Mrs. Martin need if she organizes the books in folders of 10?

Answer: _____

Mrs. Martin decides to place 100 books in each folder. How many folders does she have?

Answer: _____

Explain your thinking. _____

_____

Journal

A two-digit whole number is always a larger number than a one-digit whole number.

Is a two-digit decimal number always a larger number than a one-digit decimal number?

Circle your answer.   Yes   No

Use numbers and words to explain your answer.

_____

_____

_____

Vocabulary Activity

Read the clues. Then, draw a line to match the clue to the correct number.

I am a 6-digit number with 8 in the hundreds place.   746,832,416

I am a number with 3 in the millions place.   4,827,316.73

I am an 8-digit number with 4 in the ten thousands place.   3,823,838

I am a 7-digit number with 2 in the ones place.   318,427.38

I am a number with 7 in the hundred millions place.   43,823.2

I am a 6-digit number with 8 in the tenths place.   873,142.2

I am a number with 3 in the hundred thousands place.   37,234.8

I am a 9-digit number with 3 in the hundredths place.   842,348.27

Motivation Molly says, "Three cheers for math!"

Bigger is Better

Play *Bigger is Better* with a partner. Each player needs a game board and one die. In turn, players roll the die and record the digit rolled on one line of the game board. Players alternate play until each player has a digit written on every line. Once a digit is recorded, it cannot be changed or moved. Players answer the question that follows and discuss their thinking.

Game 1

_____ , _____ _____ _____ , _____ _____ _____ , _____ _____ _____

How could you rearrange the same 10 digits to make the LARGEST possible number? Record your answer on the line below.

_____

Game 2

_____ , _____ _____ _____ , _____ _____ _____ , _____ _____ _____

How could you rearrange the same 10 digits to make the SMALLEST possible number? Record your answer on the line below.

_____

Game 3

_____ , _____ _____ _____ , _____ _____ _____ , _____ _____ _____

In the real world, where might this number be found? Write your answer on the line below.

_____

Unit 2 Homework

1 Write the number below as an addition expression in three different ways, including expanded notation.

37,917,545

_____

_____

_____

_____

_____

2 Molly's teacher wrote this expression on the board.

100,000 + 2,000 + 500 + 150 + 17 + 0.08

Molly wrote the number in standard form. What is the correct standard form of the number?

Answer: _____

3 Use the clues to find the mystery number.

- The number has 6 digits.
- The value of the smallest digit is 0.01.
- The value of the largest digit is 8,000.
- The digit in the tens place is 2 less than the digit in the hundreds place.
- The sum of the digit in the tens place and the digit in the hundreds place is equal to the digit in the thousands place.
- The digit in the tenths place has the same value in every place.
- The remaining digit is the largest even digit.

What is the mystery number?

Answer: _____

4 Joseph saved his money to buy a tablet computer. He purchased the computer with the cash he had saved. He gave the sales clerk 4 hundred-dollar bills, 23 ten-dollar bills, 17 one-dollar bills, 46 dimes, and 19 pennies. How much money did Joseph give the sales clerk?

Answer: _____

Parent Activities

1. Write a number on a sheet of paper. Have your child write the number in many different ways (e.g., 256 may be written as two hundred fifty-six, 2 hundreds, 5 tens, and 6 ones, 25 tens and 6 ones, 200 + 50 + 6, 100 + 150 + 6, etc.).

2. Give your child a receipt from a grocery store purchase. Have your child write the total amount spent in expanded form.

3. Have your child observe the mileage on your car's odometer. Ask him/her to write this number in expanded notation, showing the value of each digit in the number. Then, give your child a calculator and have him/her demonstrate how to total the expanded notation (e.g., If the odometer reads 34,689, your child records 30,000 + 4,000 + 600 + 80 + 9. Enter these numbers on the calculator to verify that the total is equal to the observed mileage.).

1 Write the following numbers in order from least to greatest.

57,147,913   57,741,193

57,714,913   57,174,319

_____

_____

_____

2 In the 1960 presidential election, John F. Kennedy received 34,220,984 votes. His opponent, Richard M. Nixon, received 34,108,157 votes. Write a number sentence that compares the votes of the two candidates.

_____

3 The table shows the populations of 4 large cities around the world.

City	Population
Houston, TX (USA)	5,420,315
Madrid, Spain	5,427,776
Nanjing, China	5,455,115
Philadelphia, PA (USA)	5,474,820

Which city has a population that is less than the population of Nanjing but greater than the population of Houston?

Answer: _____

4 What are the three largest numbers that can be formed using the digits 2, 3, 5, 6, 8, 9, and 0? Each digit must be used only one time in each number.

_____

_____

_____

5 The table shows the populations of 3 states.

State Populations

State	Population
Arizona	6,553,255
Indiana	6,537,334
Washington	6,897,012

Write the populations of the states to complete the number sentence.

_____ > _____ > _____

6 Last year, Kelly's Candies sold 425,524,812 candy bars. Chester's Chocolates sold 425,520,736 candy bars. Which company sold more candy bars?

Answer: _____

Explain your answer.

_____

_____

Unit 3 Guided Practice

1 Which number does **NOT** make the number sentence true?

$$823,522,409 < _____$$

Ⓐ 823,629,872

Ⓑ 923,522,409

Ⓒ 823,522,409

Ⓓ 824,539,026

2 The population of Winfield County is 1,589,758. Which of the following is less than this number?

Ⓕ 1,598,758　　Ⓗ 1,589,578

Ⓖ 1,985,758　　Ⓙ 1,859,875

3 Which symbol belongs in the box to correctly complete the comparison?

$$34,692,003 \boxed{} 34,629,003$$

Ⓐ <　　　　　Ⓒ =

Ⓑ >　　　　　Ⓓ $

4 Kindra works after school to earn money to buy a car. She deposited $3,704.73 in her savings account. When her bank statement came in the mail, it showed that she had $3,740.37. Which is a true statement?

Ⓕ Kindra had less money in the bank than she deposited.

Ⓖ Kindra had more money in the bank than she deposited.

Ⓗ Kindra had the same amount of money in the bank as she deposited.

Ⓙ Kindra had no money in the bank.

Use the table to answer questions 5 and 6.

The table below shows the copper production of four countries for two years.

World Copper Production

Country	Year 1 Production (metric tons)	Year 2 Production (metric tons)
Australia	833,000	1,122,060
Chile	4,580,000	4,860,000
Indonesia	1,160,000	1,140,000
U.S.A.	1,140,000	870,000

5 According to the Year 1 data, which of the following shows the countries in order from greatest to least based on the amounts of copper produced?

Ⓐ Australia, U.S.A., Indonesia, Chile

Ⓑ Indonesia, Australia, U.S.A., Chile

Ⓒ Chile, Indonesia, U.S.A., Australia

Ⓓ Chile, Indonesia, Australia, U.S.A.

6 Which number sentence correctly compares the production of copper between Year 1 and Year 2 for Chile?

Ⓕ 1,160,000 > 1,140,000

Ⓖ 4,580,000 > 4,860,000

Ⓗ 4,580,000 < 4,860,000

Ⓙ 4,580,000 = 4,860,000

　　　　　　motivation**math**™ LEVEL 4　　　©2014 mentoring**minds**.com

1 The Lumber Supply Depot shipped between 8,500,000 and 8,700,000 nails last year. Which could **NOT** be the number of nails that were shipped?

Ⓐ 8,684,512   Ⓒ 8,689,043

Ⓑ 8,513,234   Ⓓ 8,495,001

2 Maggie works in the warehouse of a television home shopping channel. She places items on the shelves based on item numbers. The items must be in order from least to greatest.

Shopping Channel Items

Item	Item Number
Boots	56,892,078
Gloves	56,982,078
Hats	56,982,087
Purses	56,298,807

How should Maggie order the items on the shelves?

Ⓕ Boots, gloves, hats, purses

Ⓖ Purses, hats, gloves, boots

Ⓗ Hats, gloves, boots, purses

Ⓙ Purses, boots, gloves, hats

3 Which comparison statement is true?

Ⓐ 46,987 > 47,698 > 46,986

Ⓑ 46,698 < 46,986 < 46,987

Ⓒ 47,698 > 46,986 > 46,987

Ⓓ 47,698 < 46,987 < 46,986

Use the table to answer questions 4 and 5.

The table shows the iron ore production of four countries for one year.

Iron Ore Production

Ore Mining Country	Production (metric tons)
Australia	123,500,000
Brazil	170,200,000
China	123,100,000
Russia	260,400,000

4 According to information on the table, which of the following lists the countries in order of iron production from greatest to least?

Ⓕ Russia, Brazil, China, Australia

Ⓖ China, Australia, Brazil, Russia

Ⓗ Russia, Brazil, Australia, China

Ⓙ Australia, China, Brazil, Russia

5 In the same year, India reported production of iron ore in an amount greater than Brazil but less than Russia. Which of these could be the amount, in metric tons, of iron ore produced by India?

Ⓐ 245,900,000

Ⓑ 264,700,000

Ⓒ 169,300,000

Ⓓ 301,800,000

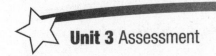
Unit 3 Assessment

Use the table to answer questions 1–3.

The table shows the amounts different cities spent on road repairs last year.

Road Repairs

City	Amount Spent
Jefferson	$1,447,456
Georgetown	$1,474,576
Wyattville	$1,675,390

1 Which lists the cities in order from least to greatest amount spent on road repairs?

Ⓐ Wyattville, Georgetown, Jefferson

Ⓑ Georgetown, Wyattville, Jefferson

Ⓒ Jefferson, Georgetown, Wyattville

Ⓓ Jefferson, Wyattville, Georgetown

2 Which comparison between the amounts spent by two cities is **NOT** true?

Ⓕ $1,447,456 < $1,474,576

Ⓖ $1,675,390 > $1,447,456

Ⓗ $1,675,390 > $1,474,576

Ⓙ $1,447,456 = $1,474,576

3 The town of Palo Pinto reported spending an amount greater than Georgetown but less than Wyattville. Which could represent the amount Palo Pinto spent on road repairs?

Ⓐ $15,227,600   Ⓒ $1,475,012

Ⓑ $1,457,500   Ⓓ $1,675,490

4 In 2007, the U.S. Mint began to produce $1 coins honoring past presidents. Two mints, one in Denver and the other in Philadelphia, produce the Presidential Dollar coins. The chart shows the coins minted for the year 2007.

2007 Presidential Dollar Coins

President	Denver	Philadelphia
Washington	163,680,000	176,680,000
Adams	112,140,000	112,420,000
Jefferson	102,810,000	100,800,000
Madison	87,780,000	84,560,000

Which number sentence does **NOT** correctly compare the coins minted in Denver and Philadelphia?

Ⓕ 163,680,000 < 176,680,000

Ⓖ 112,140,000 > 112,420,000

Ⓗ 102,810,000 > 100,800,000

Ⓙ 87,780,000 > 84,560,000

5 In 2009, the Denver Mint produced 43,540,000 Presidential Dollar coins honoring President John Tyler. The Philadelphia Mint produced 43,540,000 John Tyler dollar coins. Which number sentence correctly compares these two amounts?

Ⓐ 43,540,000 > 43,540,000

Ⓑ 43,540,000 < 43,540,000

Ⓒ 43,540,000 = 43,540,000

Ⓓ Not here

1 The table below lists four professional football teams. Use the website given to find the seating capacity of each team's stadium, and record the information on the table.

http://www.stadiumsofprofootball.com/comparisons.htm

Football Stadium Seating Capacity

NFL Teams	Stadium Seating Capacity
New Orleans Saints	
Denver Broncos	
Kansas City Chiefs	
Jacksonville Jaguars	

Use the data on the table to complete the comparison number sentences. Write >, <, or = in each circle.

New Orleans Saints $\bigcirc$ Kansas City Chiefs $\bigcirc$ Denver Broncos

Jacksonville Jaguars $\bigcirc$ Denver Broncos $\bigcirc$ New Orleans Saints

2 Use each of the following digits to create two 5-digit numbers that make the math sentence true. You may use each digit one time in each number.

Digits to use: 0, 3, 5, 8, 9

□□,□□□ > □□,□□□

Use each of the following digits to create two 6-digit numbers that make the math sentence true. You may use each digit one time in each number.

Digits to use: 0, 3, 4, 5, 8, 9

Journal

Mrs. Howard gave each student in her math group a clothespin and a drinking straw.

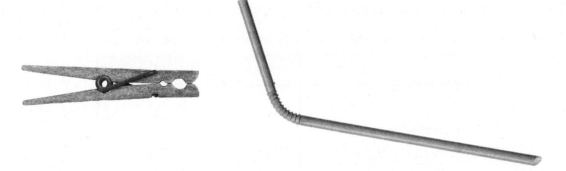

She asked the students to use the items to show ways to model the symbols for *greater than*, *less than*, and *equal to*. Explain how you could complete this activity.

_____

_____

_____

_____

Vocabulary Activity

Students often have difficulty remembering which symbol to use when comparing numbers. Use words, numbers, and pictures to create a Diagonal Definitions vocabulary card to illustrate the difference between these two comparison symbols.

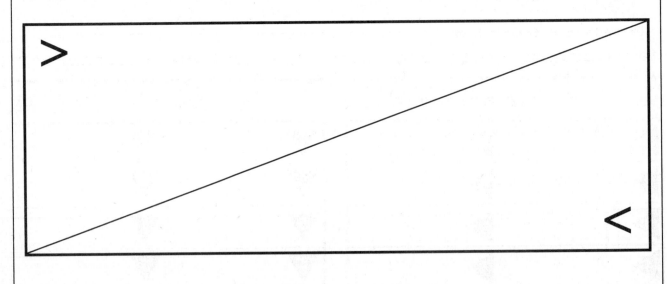

Motivation Mike says, "You've done it again!"

Comparing Numbers Brain Bender

Some digits are missing in the grid below. Use the directions to complete the grid.

- Write a digit in each blank rectangle on the grid.

- The 5-digit number in each row must be greater than the 5-digit number in the row below it.

- The 5-digit number in each column must be less than the 5-digit number in the column to its right.

There may be several solutions to the puzzle.

▽1	▽2	▽3	▽4	▽5
▶1				9
▶2	5			
▶3 4				
▶4		4		
▶5	4			

Record number sentences on the chart below to justify your solution to the puzzle.

Rows			Columns	
▶1	> ▶2		▽1	< ▽2
▶2	> ▶3		▽2	< ▽3
▶3	> ▶4		▽3	< ▽4
▶4	> ▶5		▽4	< ▽5

Unit 3 Homework

Name _____

Standard 4.2(C)–Supporting

Use the table to answer questions 1 and 2.

A geographer recorded the lengths of different rivers.

River Lengths

River	Length (miles)
Nile	4,132
Mississippi	3,902
Colorado	1,450
Amazon	3,976

1 List the rivers in order from shortest length to longest length.

_____

_____

2 The length of the Yangtze River in China is less than the length of the Amazon River but greater than the length of the Mississippi River. Write a number that could represent the length of the Yangtze River.

Answer: _____

3 Three friends kept a record of their scores on a video game for 1 month. The table shows the scores at the end of the month.

Video Game Scores

Name	Score
Alison	5,435,977
Emilee	5,432,177
Cason	5,447,113

Write a number sentence that compares the scores of the three friends.

_____

_____

4 What are the three smallest 7-digit whole numbers that can be made using only the digits 4, 3, 0, 9, 2, 8, and 5? Each digit must be used exactly one time in each number.

_____

_____

_____

✂ -

Parent Activities

1. Use a standard deck of playing cards to play a family game. Remove face cards and 10s from the deck, and shuffle the cards. Deal 6-9 cards to each player (each player receives the same number of cards). Each player arranges his/her cards to create a multi-digit number. Work together to arrange the players' numbers from least to greatest or greatest to least.

2. Use index cards or sticky notes to create number cards. Write a 4- to 9-digit number on one card. Ask your child to write a smaller number on a separate card and a larger number on a third card. Have your child arrange these numbers from least to greatest or greatest to least. On two separate notecards, write the symbol, >, (note that reversing the card shows the < symbol). Ask your child to select two numbers and compare them using < or >. Expand this activity by comparing all three numbers.

ILLEGAL TO COPY   motivation**math**™LEVEL 4

1 Amir's dad looks at the odometer on his car. He rounds the mileage to the nearest thousand and says there are about 133,000 miles on his odometer. Write a number of miles that might actually be on the car's odometer.

Answer: _____

2 Carlos read that 74,926 people attended the Texas Rangers baseball game on Friday night. Carlos rounded this number to the nearest ten thousand and reported that about 80,000 people were in attendance. Did Carlos correctly round 74,926?

Answer: _____

Explain your answer.

_____

_____

3 According to information from NASA, the space shuttle's external fuel tank has a capacity of about 500,000 gallons of fuel. Write three numbers that could represent the space shuttle's actual fuel capacity.

Answers: _____

_____

_____

4 Sonja plays video games. She scores 5,443 points on Tuesday and 7,301 points on Wednesday. Sonja rounds her scores to the nearest thousand. What expression can be used to find the best estimate of how many more points Sonja scores on Wednesday than on Tuesday?

Answer: _____

5 Locate each of the following numbers on the number line.

2,356   2,529   2,831   2,449

~~←~~|—————————|—————————|~~→~~
2,000   3,000

To the nearest thousand, which numbers round to 2,000?

Answers: _____

To the nearest thousand, which numbers round to 3,000?

Answers: _____

6 The table shows how much money the Phillips family spent on their vacation to Disney World®.

Vacation Expenses

Item	Amount Spent
Plane tickets	$1,822
Hotel rooms	$1,450
Meals	$ 985
Entertainment	$1,015

Round each value to the nearest hundred. Then, write an expression that can be used to find about how much money the family spent.

Answer: _____

_____

_____

_____

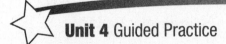

1 Ryann reads that there are 125,458 flowers planted at Pease Gardens. Ryann rounds this number to the nearest hundred thousand and tells her mom the rounded number. Which could be the number Ryann reports?

Ⓐ 100,000

Ⓒ 125,460

Ⓑ 125,000

Ⓓ 130,000

2 Marissa has 1,501 U.S. coins and 985 foreign coins. Marissa adds 2,000 and 1,000 to estimate the number of coins in her collection. Is Marissa's estimate more or less than the actual number of coins?

Ⓕ More, because she rounds both numbers up

Ⓖ More, because she rounds one number down

Ⓗ Less, because she rounds both numbers up

Ⓙ Less, because she rounds one number down

3 Look at the group of numbers.

4,379   3,793   4,499   3,542

What do these numbers have in common?

Ⓐ When rounded to the nearest ten, the numbers all round to 4,010.

Ⓑ When rounded to the nearest hundred, the numbers all round to 4,100.

Ⓒ When rounded to the nearest thousand, the numbers all round to 4,000.

Ⓓ The numbers are all greater than 3,600.

4 Captain Spence is a pilot. The table shows how many miles he flew in 3 weeks.

Flight Log

Week	Miles Flown
1	16,862
2	13,137
3	11,528

Which expression can be used to estimate, to the nearest ten thousand, the total miles Captain Spence flew?

Ⓕ 17,000 + 13,000 + 12,000

Ⓖ 20,000 + 10,000 + 10,000

Ⓗ 20,000 + 15,000 + 12,000

Ⓙ 16,900 + 13,100 + 11,500

5 When rounded to the nearest thousand, which number does **NOT** round to 8,000?

Ⓐ 8,491

Ⓒ 7,803

Ⓑ 7,682

Ⓓ 8,549

6 Look at the number line below.

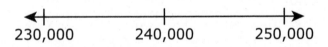

What is 232,385 rounded to the nearest ten thousand?

Ⓕ 200,000

Ⓗ 240,000

Ⓖ 230,000

Ⓙ 250,000

1 Byron says that he read a book that contains 54,000 words. He says that he rounded the actual number of words to the nearest thousand. Which could be the number of words in Byron's book?

Ⓐ 53,481   Ⓒ 54,900

Ⓑ 54,199   Ⓓ 55,310

2 Irene visited her grandparents over the summer. She flew 874 miles to see her mother's parents in June. In August, she flew 1,149 miles to see her father's parents. Which shows how to estimate, to the nearest hundred, the total miles Irene traveled?

Ⓕ 1,000 + 1,000

Ⓖ 870 + 1,150

Ⓗ 900 + 1,100

Ⓙ 900 + 1,200

3 During the first game of the season, the Houston Rockets had 37,269 fans in attendance. At the second game, there were 44,579 fans. The attendance at the third game was 38,461. The number of fans is rounded to the nearest thousand. Which list shows the rounded attendance numbers?

Ⓐ 40,000   40,000   40,000

Ⓑ 37,300   44,600   38,500

Ⓒ 37,270   44,580   38,460

Ⓓ 37,000   45,000   38,000

4 Look at the group of numbers below.

7,858   7,889   7,932

Which statement about these numbers is **NOT** correct?

Ⓕ When rounded to the nearest hundred, all the numbers round to 7,900.

Ⓖ When rounded to the nearest ten, the rounded value for each number is greater than 7,860.

Ⓗ When rounded to the nearest thousand, all the numbers round to 8,000.

Ⓙ When rounded to the nearest ten thousand, all the numbers round to 10,000.

5 Use the clues to find the mystery number.

The mystery number is —

• 1,000 when rounded to the nearest thousand, **and**

• 800 when rounded to the nearest hundred, **and**

• 770 when rounded to the nearest ten.

Which of the following could be the mystery number?

Ⓐ 741   Ⓒ 765

Ⓑ 775   Ⓓ 779

6 Two classes had a reading contest to see which class could read the most minutes. Ms. Busby's class read 12,580 minutes. Mr. Fulton's class read 14,609 minutes. Which shows the number of minutes, rounded to the nearest thousand, for Ms. Busby's class?

Ⓕ 12,000   Ⓗ 10,000

Ⓖ 13,000   Ⓙ 12,600

1 Mr. Reynolds and Mr. Montoya work for the same trucking company. Last week Mr. Reynolds drove 4,379 miles. Mr. Montoya drove 6,512 miles. Which shows these numbers rounded to the nearest hundred?

Ⓐ 4,300 and 6,500

Ⓑ 4,000 and 7,000

Ⓒ 4,400 and 6,500

Ⓓ 4,380 and 6,510

2 Preston has 479 baseball cards and 897 football cards. Preston adds 500 and 900 to estimate how many cards he has. Compare Preston's estimate with the exact total number of cards. Is the estimate more or less than the actual number of cards?

Ⓕ More, because he rounded one number down

Ⓖ Less, because he rounded both numbers up

Ⓗ More, because he rounded both numbers up

Ⓙ Less, because he rounded one number down

3 What do these numbers have in common?

  5,943   5,892   6,176   6,095

Ⓐ To the nearest thousand, the numbers all round to 6,000.

Ⓑ To the nearest hundred, the numbers all round to 6,100.

Ⓒ To the nearest ten, the numbers all round to 5,990.

Ⓓ All numbers are greater than 5,895.

4 The National Weather Service launched two weather balloons. Balloon 1 reached an altitude of 84,996 feet. Balloon 2 reached an altitude of 92,495 feet. Which statement is **NOT** true about the height reached by balloon 1?

Ⓕ When rounded to the nearest ten, balloon 1 reached a height of 85,000 feet.

Ⓖ When rounded to the nearest hundred, balloon 1 reached a height of 85,000 feet.

Ⓗ When rounded to the nearest thousand, balloon 1 reached a height of 85,000 feet.

Ⓙ When rounded to the nearest ten thousand, balloon 1 reached a height of 85,000 feet.

5 For the PTA® fund-raiser, the third-grade classes collected 23,977 pennies. The fourth-grade classes collected 34,014 pennies, and the fifth-grade classes collected 32,744 pennies. The PTA rounded the numbers of pennies to the nearest thousand. Which expression was used to estimate the total number of pennies collected by the third-, fourth-, and fifth-grade classes?

Ⓐ 23,000 + 34,000 + 32,000

Ⓑ 30,000 + 30,000 + 30,000

Ⓒ 24,000 + 34,000 + 32,700

Ⓓ 24,000 + 34,000 + 33,000

1 About 840,000 people live in Austin, Texas. Which of the following numbers could be the actual number of people who live in the capital of Texas? Circle your answer.

849,361   834,478   842,592   846,001

Explain how you found your answer.

_____

_____

_____

_____

2 Use the clues to answer the rounding riddles.

When rounded to the nearest 100, I am the smallest whole number that becomes 5,000. What number am I?

Answer: _____

When rounded to the nearest ten thousand, I am the largest whole number that becomes 40,000. What number am I?

Answer: _____

I am the sum of the following 3 numbers:

1,273 rounded to the nearest 10
1,273 rounded to the nearest 100
1,273 rounded to the nearest 1000

Answer: _____

Unit 4 Journal/Vocabulary Activity

Journal

Discuss the pros and cons of using estimation to solve a problem instead of using the actual numbers. When might you want to round a number to estimate an answer rather than actually completing the calculation to find an exact answer?

_____

_____

_____

_____

Vocabulary Activity

When estimating, we often round numbers to make computation easier. In the space below, create a word web of real-world situations in which rounding numbers is helpful.

Rounding Numbers in the Real World

Motivation Molly says, "You never cease to amaze me!"

Roll and Round

Play *Roll and Round* with a partner or small group. Each group needs 4 number cubes or dice and a pencil and paper clip to use with the spinner. Each player needs a game sheet. In turn, each player rolls 4 dice and records the numbers in the Digits Rolled column of the table. The player decides what number to create from the 4 digits and records the number in the My Number column. The player then spins the spinner to determine whether to round the number to the nearest 10, 100, or 1,000 and records the rounded number in the Rounded Number column. On each play, the player adds the new rounded number to the previous rounded number and keeps a running total. The object of the game is to be the first player to reach the target number of 10,000 without going over. Players may choose to stop rolling at any point in the game if they believe that continued play would exceed the target number of 10,000.

Spinner	Digits Rolled	My Number	Rounded Number
100 1,000 10 100 1,000 10			
	Target Number		**10,000**

Describe a strategy that could help you win the game.

_____

_____

1 Heidi and Shannon made bracelets from colored bands. Heidi used 1,126 bands. Shannon used 1,264 bands for her bracelets. To the nearest hundred, what values represent the bands Heidi and Shannon used?

Answers: _____ and _____

2 The table shows the average prices of homes in four states in the United States.

Average Home Prices

State	Average Home Price ($)
Colorado	564,632
Nevada	412,201
New York	698,344
Arizona	328,685

Round each price to the nearest ten thousand.

Colorado _____

Nevada _____

New York _____

Arizona _____

3 Gina's family went on vacation. They traveled 325 miles the first day, 481 miles the second day, and 119 miles the third day. If these distances are rounded to the nearest hundred, what expression can be used to find an estimate of how many more miles the family traveled on the second day than the first day?

Answer: _____

4 The population of a Texas city is 96,451. What is this number rounded to the nearest hundred, thousand, and ten thousand?

Hundred _____

Thousand _____

Ten thousand _____

What is the population of your hometown?

Answer: _____

Round this number to the greatest place value.

Answer: _____

Parent Activities

1. While driving, have your child estimate the mileage from Point A to Point B. At the end of the trip, check the actual mileage and discuss whether or not the estimate was reasonable.

2. Use everyday numbers to practice rounding with your child. Ask questions such as, "I heard on the news that 214,802 people visited the water park this summer. What is this number rounded to the nearest ten thousand?"

3. Write a 6-digit number at the top of a sheet of paper. Ask your child to round the original number to the nearest ten. Below that, have your child round this number to the nearest hundred, then round to the nearest thousand, and so on until it is not possible to round any more. Discuss how the rounded number changes (e.g., If the original number is 756,938, the rounded numbers would be: 756,940 → 756,900 → 757,000 → 760,000 → 800,000.).

1 Lee's Bakery cut a square cake into 100 equal bite-sized pieces to give as samples at the grand opening. In the first hour, 37 pieces were eaten. Shade the decimal model to show how much of the whole cake was eaten in the first hour.

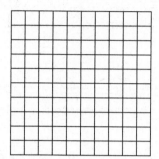

Write the decimal number represented by the model.

Answer: _____

What decimal number represents the part of the whole cake that was **NOT** eaten?

Answer: _____

2 Lindy went to a movie. She bought popcorn and a soda at the snack bar and paid with a $10 bill. Lindy received the money shown below as change.

Write the decimal number that represents Lindy's change.

Answer: _____

3 Mr. Luna filled his gas tank on Saturday. On Tuesday, he glanced at the gas gauge on his car. The shaded portion of the model shows the gas that remained in his tank.

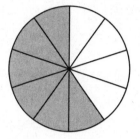

Write the decimal number that represents the part of Mr. Luna's tank that contains gas.

Answer: _____

What decimal number represents the part of the tank that is empty?

Answer: _____

4 A decimal number is represented by the shaded model below. Each completely shaded square represents one whole.

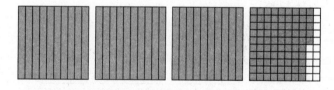

Write the decimal number for this model.

Answer: _____

5 Peyton buys a game at the toy store. Including tax, Peyton pays $4.57 for the game. Draw a picture to represent the amount Peyton pays for the game.

1 Tammy's mother ordered 3 pizzas. The shaded parts of the models represent the amount of pizza the family ate.

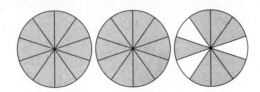

Which decimal number is represented by the model?

Ⓐ 27.0   Ⓒ 0.27

Ⓑ 2.3   Ⓓ 2.7

2 Eduardo shades a decimal square to create a picture of a rabbit.

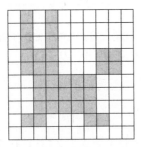

What decimal number is represented by Eduardo's shaded picture?

Ⓕ 0.53   Ⓗ 0.35

Ⓖ 3.5   Ⓙ 35

3 Anna shades a model to show her piano practice time. Each completely shaded square represents 1 hour. Anna's model for last week is shown below.

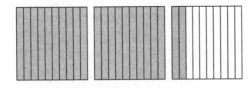

Which shows Anna's practice time last week?

Ⓐ 22 hours   Ⓒ 0.22 hour

Ⓑ 2.2 hours   Ⓓ 2.22 hours

4 Hallie paid $4.52 for a burger and fries. Which collection of money represents this amount?

Ⓕ

Ⓖ

Ⓗ

Ⓙ

5 Jan went grocery shopping with her dad. Dad paid for the purchase with a $20 bill and received an amount of change represented by the shaded model.

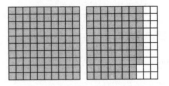

How much change did Jan's dad receive?

Ⓐ $1.78   Ⓒ $1.50

Ⓑ $1.25   Ⓓ $1.35

1 John ran 1.43 miles on Monday, 1.34 miles on Tuesday, and 1.65 miles on Wednesday. Which of the following correctly illustrates the number of miles John ran on Wednesday?

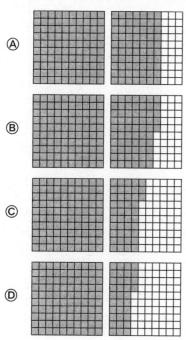

2 Kadie had an orange juice carton that was almost empty. The shaded part of the model shows the amount of juice left in Kadie's carton.

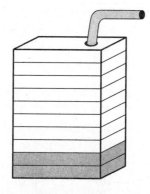

Which decimal represents the amount of juice left in Kadie's carton?

Ⓕ 0.02   Ⓗ 1.2

Ⓖ 2.0   Ⓙ 0.2

3 Guillermo saved the amount of money shown by recycling aluminum cans. What number does the money represent?

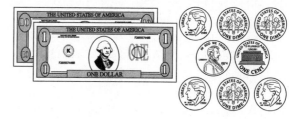

Ⓐ $2.26

Ⓑ $11.62

Ⓒ $11.25

Ⓓ $21.62

4 Which decimal number is shown by the shaded model?

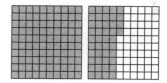

Ⓕ 1.44

Ⓖ 10.4

Ⓗ 1.04

Ⓙ 14.0

5 Which decimal model does **NOT** show 0.8 shaded?

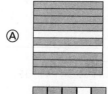
Ⓐ

Ⓒ

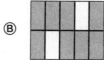
Ⓑ

Ⓓ

Unit 5 Assessment

1 Which decimal model is equal to 0.35?

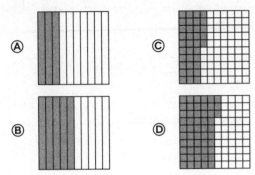

Ⓐ   Ⓒ

Ⓑ   Ⓓ

2 Three students drew models to represent the decimal 0.9.

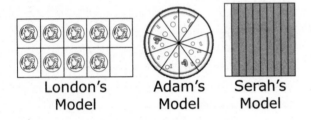

London's Model   Adam's Model   Serah's Model

Which student did **NOT** correctly represent the decimal number 0.9?

Ⓕ London

Ⓖ Adam

Ⓗ Serah

Ⓙ All students' models are correct.

3 Luis correctly shaded a decimal number with a value greater than 0.7 but less than 0.8. Which model could be Luis' decimal number?

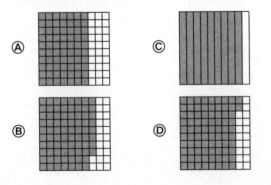

Ⓐ   Ⓒ

Ⓑ   Ⓓ

4 The table shows the prices of 3 different ice cream treats.

Ice Cream Treats

Treat	Price
Nutty Fudge Bar	$2.53
Gooey Caramel Cone	$2.64
Pecan Swirl Cup	$2.45

Which collection of money shows the exact amount needed to buy a Pecan Swirl Cup?

Ⓕ

Ⓖ

Ⓗ

Ⓙ

Name _____

Standard 4.2(E)–Supporting

Unit 5 Critical Thinking

1 Members of the student council decorated the windows of the school for the fall carnival. The girls decorated the windows on the bottom floor with plastic sunflowers. The boys decorated the windows on the top floor with paper pumpkins. All windows were the same size. Each window on the top floor was divided into ten vertical panes, and each window on the bottom floor was divided into one hundred small square panes. The boys put pumpkins on 0.2 of the first window, 0.5 of the second window, and 0.6 of the third window. The girls put sunflowers on 0.36 of the first window, 0.62 of the second window, and 0.13 of the third window. Which floor had the greatest part of the windows decorated?

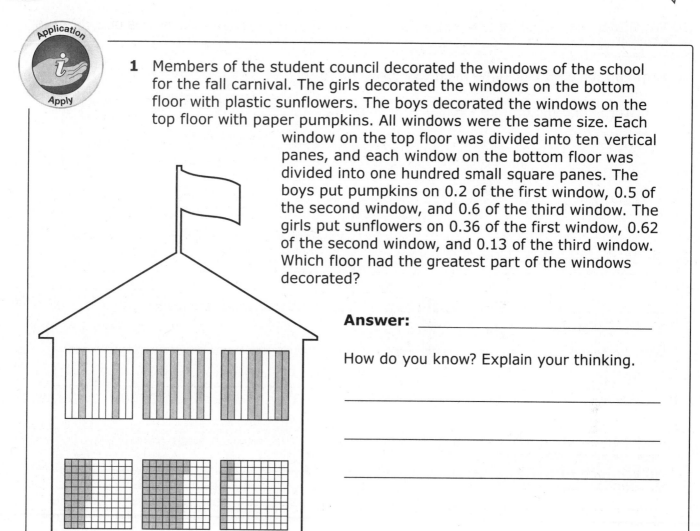

Answer: _____

How do you know? Explain your thinking.

_____

_____

_____

2 Complete these statements.

I would rather have 300 _____ than 0.03 _____ .

I would rather have 0.06 _____ than 600 _____ .

Explain your reasoning.

_____

_____

_____

©2014 mentoringminds.com

Journal

How can base 10 blocks be used to represent $6.49?

Use words and pictures to explain your thinking.

_____

_____

_____

_____

Vocabulary Activity

A decimal number is represented by the base 10 blocks shown below.

Color the hundredths red.
Color the ones green.
Color the tenths purple.

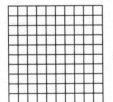 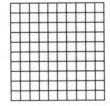 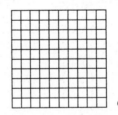 •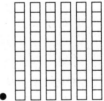

Write the decimal number shown by these base 10 blocks.

Answer: _____

What bills and coins could be used to represent this decimal number?

Answer: _____

         motivation**math**™LEVEL 4

Motivation Mike says, "This brightens my day!"

Color Them All

Play *Color Them All* with a partner. Each player uses a hundred grid and different colored pencils or crayons. Use a pencil and paper clip to create a spinner. Players take turns spinning the spinner and coloring the number of squares as determined by the spin. Players use a different color each turn to show the different decimals. If a player does not have enough squares to color the decimal spun, the player loses the turn. The winner is the first person to completely color the hundred chart exactly.

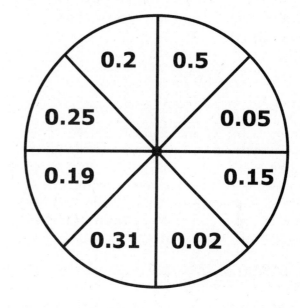

Player 1

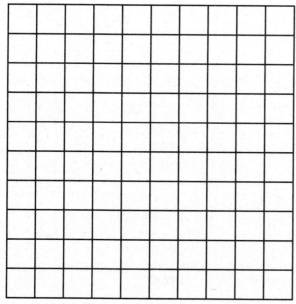

Player 2

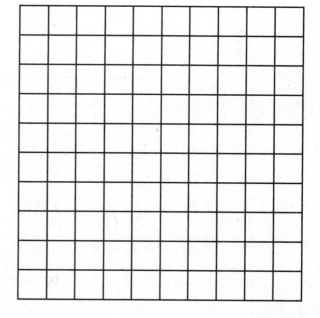

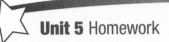

1 Melanie had $3.59 left from her allowance after she went to a movie with her cousin. Shade the grids to represent Melanie's money.

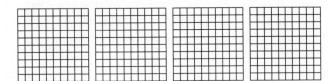

2 For homework, Mark wrote a word problem and illustrated it by shading these grids.

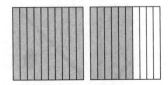

When Mark got to school the next day, he realized he had left his word problem at home. He wrote another problem to turn in with his picture. What word problem could Mark have written?

_____

_____

_____

_____

3 Phoebe earns extra money by walking her neighbor's dog. Phoebe counted the money she earned last week.

How much money did Phoebe earn last week?

Answer: _____

4 The meteorologist reported that the city received two and three tenths inches of precipitation last week. Draw a model to represent this decimal number.

✂ --

Parent Activities

1. Look at the sports section of the newspaper, and find statistics that contain decimal numbers from a sporting event (e.g., track and field events, swimming events, baseball batting averages, etc.). Have your child sketch and shade a grid to represent the decimal number shaded (limit to tenths and hundredths).

2. Use food labels and money to discuss the values of digits in the decimal numbers to the tenths and hundredths places (e.g., a water bottle with 16.9 fluid ounces, a $3.25 expense, a can with a weight of 22.75 ounces, etc.). Reinforce that digits to the left of the decimal point represent whole numbers, and digits to the right of the decimal point represent amounts less than one whole.

3. Use multicolored food items such as fruity cereal or colored chocolate candies to model decimals. Spread out a handful of the food. Ask your child to build a group of certain colors (e.g., "Show me a group of 10 that is 0.7 red and 0.3 yellow.").

Name _____

1 Jack weighed his pet hamster on a digital scale. The hamster's weight was a decimal number greater than 1.4 ounces but less than 1.65 ounces. Shade the model below to show what Jack's hamster might weigh.

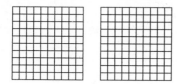

Record the weight on the line in the number sentence below. Then complete the comparison by placing > or < in each circle.

1.4 ◯ _____ ◯ 1.65

2 Mr. Ramirez timed Nico as he swam three laps in the pool. Nico completed the first lap in 35.7 seconds. He swam the second lap in 35.07 seconds and the third lap in 35.53 seconds. Nico wrote the three times on a place value chart.

3	5	.	7	
3	5	.	0	7
3	5	.	5	3
Tens	Ones	.	Tenths	Hundredths

Write a number sentence to compare Nico's swim times on laps 1 and 2.

Answer: _____

Write a number sentence that compares Nico's swim times on laps 2 and 3.

Answer: _____

3 The shaded models represent three different decimal numbers.

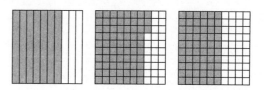

Write the decimal numbers in order from least to greatest.

_____   _____   _____

4 Mason and Hannah compared the money in their pockets.

Mason said, "I have more money than you because I have 6 dimes."

Hannah said, "I have more money than you because I have 60 pennies."

Shade the model to show Mason's money and Hannah's money. Then write the decimal number that represents each child's money on the line below the model.

Mason's Money   Hannah's Money

_____   _____

Write a number sentence that compares the two amounts.

Answer: _____

Which child is correct?

Answer: _____

Unit 6 Guided Practice

1 The shaded models represent the decimal numbers 0.8 and 0.10.

Which comparison is true?

Ⓐ 0.8 = 0.10

Ⓑ 0.8 > 0.10

Ⓒ 0.8 < 0.10

Ⓓ 0.10 > 0.8

2 Jacob records the distances his teammates jumped in the long jump at a track meet. The coach asks him to order the 4 distances from least to greatest.

   7.38   7.51   7.4   7.26

Jacob draws a number line to help with the task.

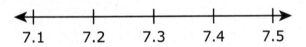

Which shows the correct order of the distances from least to greatest?

Ⓕ 7.38   7.4   7.51   7.26

Ⓖ 7.51   5.4   7.38   7.26

Ⓗ 7.26   7.38   7.51   7.4

Ⓙ 7.26   7.38   7.4   7.51

3 Veronica, Terry, Gus, and Stuart each shaded a decimal model. Look at the decimal numbers represented by the shaded models.

Veronica   Terry   Gus   Stuart

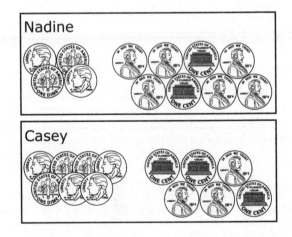

The students arranged the models in order from greatest to least. Which of the following is the correct order?

Ⓐ 0.50   0.48   0.32   0.30

Ⓑ 0.50   0.48   0.30   0.32

Ⓒ 0.30   0.48   0.50   0.32

Ⓓ 0.30   0.32   0.48   0.50

4 Nadine and Casey compare the numbers of dimes and pennies in their wallets.

Nadine

Casey

Which of the following number sentences correctly compares the total values of the coins?

Ⓕ $76 > $48   Ⓗ $0.48 < $0.76

Ⓖ $0.67 < $0.84   Ⓙ $4.08 < $7.06

motivation**math**™LEVEL 4

Name _____

Standard 4.2(F) — Supporting

Unit 6 Independent Practice

1 Which model correctly represents the comparison 0.3 > 0.03?

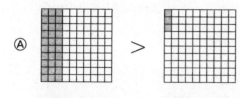

Ⓐ

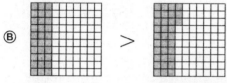

Ⓑ

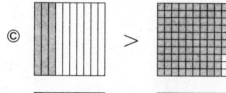

Ⓒ

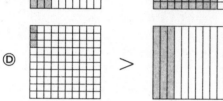

Ⓓ

2 Kylie uses a number line to order 4 decimal numbers from greatest to least.

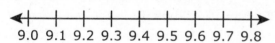

Which list shows 4 decimals ordered correctly?

Ⓕ 9.76 9.6 9.58 9.63

Ⓖ 9.76 9.58 9.63 9.6

Ⓗ 9.76 9.63 9.6 9.58

Ⓙ 9.58 9.6 9.63 9.76

3 Which symbol can be placed in the circle to make the number sentence true?

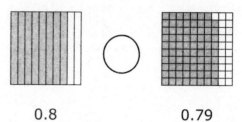

0.8   0.79

Ⓐ <

Ⓑ >

Ⓒ +

Ⓓ =

4 Leon shaded 3 figures to represent decimal numbers.

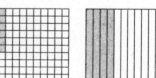

Which number sentence correctly compares the 3 numbers?

Ⓕ 0.6 > 0.4 > 0.60

Ⓖ 0.06 < 0.5 < 0.06

Ⓗ 0.06 < 0.4 < 0.60

Ⓙ 0.6 > 0.04 > 0.60

©2014 mentoring**minds**.com

Unit 6 Assessment

1 Which decimal models correctly represent the comparison 0.7 = 0.70?

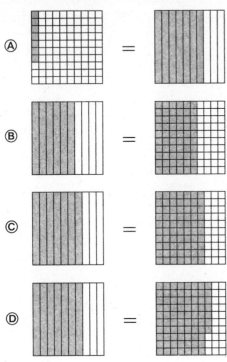

2 Arianna shades models to represent 4 decimal numbers as shown.

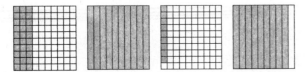

Figure 1   Figure 2   Figure 3   Figure 4

She arranges the figures in order from greatest decimal number to least decimal number. How does Arianna arrange the figures?

Ⓕ   1.0   0.9   0.30   0.09

Ⓖ   0.09   0.30   0.9   1.0

Ⓗ   1.0   0.9   0.09   0.30

Ⓙ   0.9   0.09   0.30   1.0

3 Leland's dog had 2 puppies. Patches weighed 1.1 pounds, and Skipper weighed 1.01 pounds, as shown by the models.

Patches   Skipper

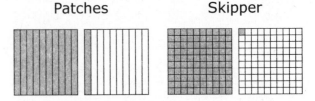

Which number sentence correctly compares the weights of the 2 puppies?

Ⓐ   1.1 = 1.01

Ⓑ   1.01 > 1.1

Ⓒ   1.01 < 1.1

Ⓓ   1.1 < 1.01

4 Alvin sells fresh fruit at the Farmers' Market. He uses a digital scale to find the weights of the fruit he sells. On Saturday, he sold 4 cantaloupes that weighed 3.27 pounds, 3.09 pounds, 3.18 pounds, and 3.1 pounds. Alvin uses a number line to order the weights of the cantaloupes from lightest to heaviest.

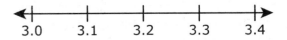
3.0   3.1   3.2   3.3   3.4

Which correctly lists the weights of the cantaloupes from lightest to heaviest?

Ⓕ   3.27   3.18   3.09   3.1

Ⓖ   3.27   3.1   3.18   3.09

Ⓗ   3.09   3.1   3.27   3.18

Ⓙ   3.09   3.1   3.18   3.27

motivation**math**™LEVEL 4
©2014 mentoring**minds**.com

1 Harrison played a bowling game on his Wii® game system. At the end of round one, 3 of the 10 pins were left standing. At the end of round two, none of the 10 pins were left standing, and after round three, only one pin was left standing. Place an X to show the pins Harrison knocked down in each round. Below each model, record the decimal number that represents the part of each whole set of pins Harrison knocked down.

Round 1	Round 2	Round 3

_____	_____	_____

List the decimal numbers in order from least to greatest.

_____   _____   _____

2 Marisol's teacher asks her to write five decimal numbers that are between 5.1 and 5.2. Marisol draws this number line to help her find the answers. Use the number line to locate and label five decimal numbers that Marisol might write.

5   5.1   5.2

Explain your answer.

_____

_____

_____

Journal

Think of the U.S. coins *penny*, *nickel*, *dime*, *quarter*, and *half dollar*.
Explain how the values of these five coins represent decimal numbers.

_____

_____

_____

_____

_____

Vocabulary Activity

Select two vocabulary terms from the word box. Write the words in the center circles
of the graphic organizers below. Then complete the sections around each circle to tell
what you know about each word you chose.

Word Box		
decimal point	greater than	less than
equal	hundredths	tenths

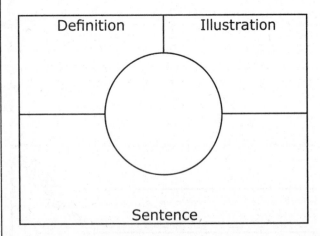

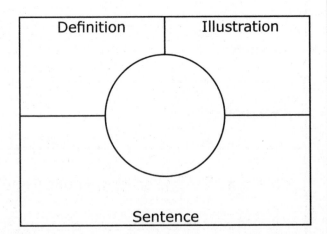

motivation**math**™ LEVEL 4
©2014 mentoring**minds**.com

Motivation Molly says, "You're on the right track!"

Zapped by a Six

Play *Zapped by a Six* with a partner. Each pair needs one number cube or die, a game board, and a pencil. In turn, players roll the number cube/die and record the digit rolled on any blank line in Round 1. If the player rolls a six, the digit is "zapped," and the player must record a zero on a line. Once a digit is written, it may not be erased or moved. When each player has rolled and recorded 3 digits, the players decide which resulting number is larger. The player with the larger number writes his/her name in the final column. The winner is the player with his/her name written more often in the final column.

6	Player 1 writes numbers here.	Player 2 writes numbers here.	Player with larger number writes name here.
Round 1	___ . ___ ___	___ . ___ ___	
Round 2	___ . ___ ___	___ . ___ ___	
Round 3	___ . ___ ___	___ . ___ ___	
Round 4	___ . ___ ___	___ . ___ ___	
Round 5	___ . ___ ___	___ . ___ ___	
Round 6	___ . ___ ___	___ . ___ ___	
Round 7	___ . ___ ___	___ . ___ ___	

What is a strategy for winning this game? _____ 6

_____

1 A marble rolls 0.78 yard, and a penny rolls 0.23 yard. Write a number sentence that compares the two distances.

Answer: _____

Use the number line to justify your answer.

0   1

2 Amanda and Gabby bake bread. Amanda takes 0.4 of the bread home. Gabby takes 0.6 of the bread home. In the space below, draw a model that shows how much bread each girl takes home.

Write a number sentence to compare the amounts of bread the girls take home.

Answer: _____

3 Leo records his weekly weight loss on a grid. The shaded grids show Leo's progress over 4 weeks. Each grid represents 1 pound.

Week 1   Week 2   Week 3   Week 4

_____   _____   _____   _____

Write Leo's weekly weight loss on the line beneath each model. Then write the decimal numbers in order from greatest to least amount of weight lost.

_____   _____   _____   _____

In week 5, Mr. Leo lost the same amount of weight that he lost in week 3. Compare Leo's weight loss by writing >, <, or = in the blank spaces.

Week 1 loss _____ Week 2 loss

Week 2 loss _____ Week 3 loss

Week 3 loss _____ Week 4 loss

Week 4 loss _____ Week 5 loss

Week 5 loss _____ Week 3 loss

Parent Activities

1. Find decimal numbers in the newspaper sports and business sections. Ask your child to compare the decimal numbers and write them in order from least to greatest or greatest to least.

2. Place 10 dimes and 10 pennies into each of two lunch bags. Give your child one lunch bag and keep the other. Each person removes a handful of coins from the bag and records the values. Ask your child to use the symbols <, >, or = to write a number sentence that compares the amounts.

3. Play *Dec 'Em All* with your child using 3 number cubes/dice and 2 sheets of paper. Player 1 rolls three number cubes and uses the numbers to create the largest possible number with a ones place, tenths place, and hundredths place (e.g., 4.21, 6.42, 5.51). Player 2 repeats the process. The player with the larger number wins the round. Continue playing several more rounds. Have your child state the value of each digit in the number.

Use the following information to answer questions 1 and 2.

A cup of coffee at a diner costs $1.29.

1 Which of the following fractions is equivalent to the cost of a cup of coffee?

Ⓐ $\frac{1}{29}$

Ⓒ $1\frac{29}{100}$

Ⓑ $1\frac{29}{10}$

Ⓓ $1\frac{1}{29}$

2 Mr. Baskin buys a cup of coffee and pays with two $1 bills. He receives $\frac{71}{100}$ of a dollar in change. Which model represents Mr. Baskin's change?

Ⓕ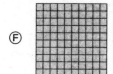

Ⓖ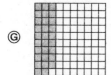

Ⓗ

Ⓙ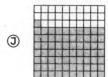

3 Which equation is **NOT** true?

Ⓐ $41.10 = 41\frac{10}{10}$

Ⓑ $23.45 = 23\frac{45}{100}$

Ⓒ $6.7 = 6\frac{7}{10}$

Ⓓ $7.10 = 7\frac{10}{100}$

4 For the school fund-raiser, each student was asked to sell a box that contained 10 rolls of wrapping paper. Carlotta sold 8 rolls, or $\frac{8}{10}$ of a box. Which is the best decimal representation of the part of the box that Carlotta sold?

Ⓕ 0.008

Ⓖ 0.08

Ⓗ 0.8

Ⓙ 8

5 A bricklayer brought 100 bricks to Carroll Elementary to edge the front sidewalk of the school. He used 96 of the 100 bricks. Which shows how this amount can be represented?

Ⓐ $9\frac{6}{10}$ or 9.6

Ⓑ $\frac{96}{100}$ or 0.96

Ⓒ 9.6 or $\frac{9.6}{10}$

Ⓓ 9.06 or $9\frac{6}{100}$

6 Makensie's family ordered 9 large pizzas for a family reunion. Each pizza was cut into 10 slices. The group ate 6 whole pizzas and $\frac{5}{10}$ of another pizza. Which decimal number tells how much pizza was eaten at the reunion?

Ⓕ 9.65

Ⓖ 6.05

Ⓗ 6.5

Ⓙ 0.65

Unit 7 Assessment

1 Terrin shaded the decimal model below to represent the time, in hours, that she spent on homework last night.

Which number is also represented by Terrin's model?

Ⓐ $1\frac{4}{100}$

Ⓑ $1\frac{40}{10}$

Ⓒ $1\frac{04}{100}$

Ⓓ $1\frac{40}{100}$

2 Ms. Chan planted 100 tulip bulbs in the garden. Red tulips made up 0.57 of the bulbs. How could Ms. Chan write the fractional part of the garden that was red tulips?

Ⓕ $\frac{5}{7}$

Ⓖ $5\frac{7}{10}$

Ⓗ $\frac{57}{100}$

Ⓙ $\frac{57}{10}$

3 Eliza completed $\frac{34}{100}$ of a jigsaw puzzle by herself. Daryl completed the remaining 0.66 of the puzzle. Which pair shows the decimal number that represents the part of the puzzle Eliza completed and the fraction of the puzzle Daryl completed?

Ⓐ 0.34 and $\frac{66}{100}$

Ⓑ 100.34 and $\frac{6}{10}$

Ⓒ 3.4 and $6\frac{6}{10}$

Ⓓ 34.00 and $\frac{66}{100}$

4 According to Kiki, five-tenths of the students in her gymnastics class can do a cartwheel. Which decimal number represents the students in Kiki's class who can do cartwheels?

Ⓕ 5.0

Ⓖ 50

Ⓗ 0.05

Ⓙ 0.5

5 John David has 100 baseball cards that he wants to put in an album. Twenty-three of his cards are rookie cards. Which shaded model represents the part of John David's baseball cards that are rookie cards?

Ⓐ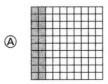

Ⓑ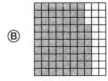

Ⓒ

Ⓓ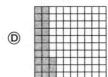

6 Ahmed correctly answered $\frac{9}{10}$ of the questions on his science test. Which decimal number represents the part of the questions Ahmed answered correctly on the test?

Ⓕ $\frac{0.9}{10}$

Ⓖ 0.90

Ⓗ 0.09

Ⓙ 9.0

motivation**math**™ LEVEL 4

1 Mrs. Dodd gave her students a hundred chart. She asked them to color numbers on the chart using a pattern of their choice.

- Beth colored all the odd numbers. Write a number sentence that shows the fraction of the chart Beth colored and the equivalent decimal.

  Answer: _____

- Cora colored the 2-digit numbers. Write a number sentence that shows the fraction of the chart Cora colored and the equivalent decimal.

  Answer: _____

- Damian colored all the numbers that contain the digit 1. Write a number sentence that shows the fraction of the chart Damian colored and the equivalent decimal.

  Answer: _____

1	2	3	4	5	6	7	8	9	10
11	12	13	14	15	16	17	18	19	20
21	22	23	24	25	26	27	28	29	30
31	32	33	34	35	36	37	38	39	40
41	42	43	44	45	46	47	48	49	50
51	52	53	54	55	56	57	58	59	60
61	62	63	64	65	66	67	68	69	70
71	72	73	74	75	76	77	78	79	80
81	82	83	84	85	86	87	88	89	90
91	92	93	94	95	96	97	98	99	100

2 Roderick used a meter stick to measure the dimensions of his teacher's filing cabinet. The model shows a reduced size of the meter stick.

10   20   30   40   50   60   70   80   90

He found that the height of the filing cabinet is 78 centimeters. What fraction of a meter is the height of the filing cabinet?

Answer: _____

What decimal number can be used to represent the height, in meters, of the filing cabinet?

Answer: _____

What standard unit of measure is exactly A: 0.1 meter? B: 0.01 meter?

Answers: A _____   B _____

Journal

Analysis

i

Analyze

The prefix *deci-* means *one-tenth*, and the prefix *centi-* means *one-hundredth*. Use this information to explain why a dime could be renamed *deci-dollar* and a penny could be renamed *centi-dollar*.

_____

_____

_____

_____

_____

Vocabulary Activity

Select either *decimal* or *fraction*, and create an acrostic poem. Each letter of the selected word should provide a real-world example that represents something about a decimal or fraction. For example, the D in *decimal* could be "Dime is equivalent to $0.10 of a dollar" or the N in *fraction* could explain that "Nickel is $\frac{5}{100}$ of a dollar."

_____

_____

_____

_____

_____

_____

_____

_____

motivation**math**™ LEVEL 4
©2014 mentoring**minds**.com

Motivation Mike says, "You make this look easy!"

Decimal Mosaic

The large square is partitioned into 100 small squares. Each small square represents $\frac{1}{100}$ or 0.01 of the large square. Use 5–7 different colors to create a decimal mosaic by coloring complete squares. Do not divide small squares or color parts of squares. When the decimal mosaic is finished, complete the chart at the bottom of the page.

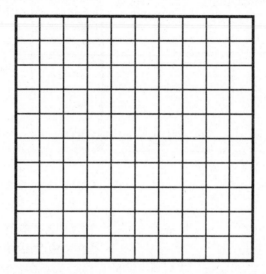

In the first column, list each color used in the decimal mosaic. In the second column, record the number of squares of each color. In the third column, write the fraction that represents the fractional part of the large square for each color. In the last column, record the corresponding decimal number.

Color	Number of Squares	Fraction	Decimal

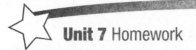
1   Phaedra bought a candy bar for $1.80. She represented this amount by shading the model below.

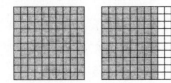

What two mixed numbers are also represented by Phaedra's model?

Answers: _____   _____

2   Beau uses this spinner in a game.

What fraction of the sections on Beau's spinner contain an odd number?

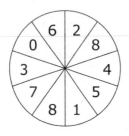

Answer: _____

What decimal represents this fractional part?

Answer: _____

3   Tim drops 100 M&M'S® candies in a jar. He charts how many pieces of each color he places in the jar. Complete the chart to show the fractional part of the candy represented by each color and the corresponding decimal number.

Color of Candy	Number of Pieces	Fraction Number	Decimal Number
Yellow	26		
Red	34		
Green	10		
Blue	7		
Brown	23		

4   Katie creates a decimal model to represent $\frac{4}{5}$. In the space beside Katie's model, create a model to represent a decimal number equivalent to $\frac{4}{5}$.

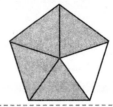

✂ -

Parent Activities

1. Hold up 8 fingers. Ask your child, "What fraction of my 10 fingers are up?" Your child should answer, "eight-tenths." Ask your child to write this fraction as a decimal number with the same value. Continue to hold up different numbers of fingers, and have your child identify the fraction of fingers shown. Then state, "Show me six-tenths of your fingers." Your child should hold up 6 fingers. Continue, each time recording the fraction and equivalent decimal.

2. Use only dimes and/or pennies to make groups of change. Ask your child to identify the fraction of a dollar in each group (e.g., If you place 7 dimes in a group, the fraction would be $\frac{7}{10}$, $\frac{70}{100}$, or 0.70.). Remind your child that dimes represent tenths and pennies represent hundredths of a dollar. Extend the activity, using different combinations of dimes and pennies (e.g., 3 dimes and 8 pennies = $\frac{38}{100}$ or 0.38).

3. Go on a decimal scavenger hunt with your child. Look for examples of decimals in your home, at the store, in the newspaper, in the kitchen, etc. Use the opportunity to discuss what decimal numbers mean and how we use decimals in everyday life. Work together with your child to write the decimal amounts as fractions (e.g., $4.82 = 4\frac{82}{100}$ or $6.8 = 6\frac{8}{10}$).

1 Dee's mother gave her $\frac{4}{7}$ of a pan of brownies. She and her 3 brothers equally shared them, as shown by the shaded part of the figure below. Decompose $\frac{4}{7}$ to show what fraction of the brownies each person received.

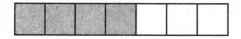

$\frac{4}{7}$ = _____ + _____ + _____ + _____

2 Travis downloads music to his MP3 player. Two-sixths of the music he downloads is rock music, and $\frac{3}{6}$ of the music is country music. What fraction of the music Travis downloads is either rock or country music?

Answer: _____

Use two different colors to shade the fraction model below to show your answer.

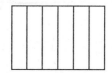

Write an equation that represents all the fraction model.

Answer: _____

3 Mario paints $\frac{3}{10}$ of the fence with red paint and $\frac{4}{10}$ of the fence with blue paint.

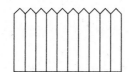

What fraction of the fence does Mario leave unpainted?

Answer: _____

4 Use numbers and pictures to show two different ways to decompose the fraction $\frac{3}{4}$.

Record two equations to show how you decomposed $\frac{3}{4}$.

Answers: _____

_____

5 Marina baked 2 cookie cakes for her party. Each cookie cake was cut into sixths. Marina ate 2 pieces, Anna ate 3 pieces, Levon ate 2 pieces, and the other 3 guests each ate 1 piece of cookie cake at Marina's party. Shade the model to show the cake eaten at the party.

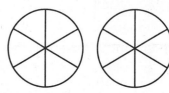

What improper fraction is represented by the shaded model?

Answer: _____

Decompose the total amount of cake eaten into an expression with fractions that represent the amount eaten by each person.

Answer: _____

1 Melanie baked one dozen holiday cookies. Four cookies were stars, three cookies were candy canes, and the rest of the cookies were snowflakes.

Which of the following equations does **NOT** show the part of the cookies that were stars and candy canes?

Ⓐ $\frac{4}{12} + \frac{3}{12} = \frac{7}{12}$

Ⓑ $\frac{1}{12} + \frac{1}{12} + \frac{1}{12} + \frac{1}{12} + \frac{3}{12} = \frac{7}{12}$

Ⓒ $\frac{4}{12} + \frac{1}{12} + \frac{1}{12} + \frac{1}{12} = \frac{7}{12}$

Ⓓ $\frac{4}{12} + \frac{5}{12} + \frac{3}{12} = \frac{12}{12}$

2 Luigi's Pizza uses $\frac{1}{4}$ cup each of 6 different toppings on the "everything" pizza. Which number sentence shows the total cups of toppings on the pizza?

Ⓕ $\frac{6}{4} + \frac{6}{4} + \frac{6}{4} + \frac{6}{4} + \frac{6}{4} + \frac{6}{4} = \frac{24}{4}$

Ⓖ $\frac{1}{4} + \frac{1}{4} + \frac{1}{4} + \frac{1}{4} + \frac{1}{4} + \frac{1}{4} = \frac{6}{24}$

Ⓗ $\frac{1}{4} + \frac{1}{4} + \frac{1}{4} + \frac{1}{4} + \frac{1}{4} + \frac{1}{4} = \frac{6}{4}$

Ⓙ $\frac{1}{6} + \frac{1}{6} + \frac{1}{6} + \frac{1}{6} = \frac{4}{6}$

3 Kiefer noticed that the chocolate bars sold at the school fundraiser were divided into 6 equal parts. Over two days, he and his brother ate a total of $\frac{20}{6}$ candy bars. Which model below shows the candy Kiefer and his brother ate?

Ⓐ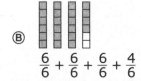
$\frac{6}{6} + \frac{6}{6} + \frac{3}{6}$

Ⓑ
$\frac{6}{6} + \frac{6}{6} + \frac{6}{6} + \frac{4}{6}$

Ⓒ
$\frac{5}{6} + \frac{5}{6} + \frac{5}{6} + \frac{5}{6}$

Ⓓ
$\frac{6}{6} + \frac{6}{6} + \frac{6}{6} + \frac{6}{6} + \frac{2}{6}$

4 Avery practiced the trombone a total of $\frac{11}{12}$ of an hour. He divided his practice time into smaller parts. Which of the following does **NOT** show a way Avery could have decomposed his practice time?

Ⓕ $\frac{11}{12} = \frac{1}{12} + \frac{1}{12} + \frac{1}{12} + \frac{3}{12} + \frac{5}{12}$

Ⓖ $\frac{11}{12} = \frac{5}{12} + \frac{2}{12} + \frac{2}{12} + \frac{3}{12}$

Ⓗ $\frac{11}{12} = \frac{6}{12} + \frac{2}{12} + \frac{3}{12}$

Ⓙ $\frac{11}{12} = \frac{4}{12} + \frac{7}{12}$

motivation**math**™ LEVEL 4

1 Beth and Mick help Tracy return seven books to the library. Beth carries $\frac{3}{7}$ of the books, and Mick carries $\frac{2}{7}$ of the books.

Which equation represents the fraction of the books Beth and Mick carry to the library?

Ⓐ $\frac{1}{7} + \frac{1}{7} = \frac{2}{7}$

Ⓑ $\frac{1}{7} + \frac{1}{7} + \frac{1}{7} + \frac{1}{7} + \frac{1}{7} = \frac{5}{7}$

Ⓒ $\frac{5}{7} + \frac{2}{7} = \frac{7}{7}$

Ⓓ $\frac{3}{7} + \frac{2}{7} + \frac{1}{7} = \frac{6}{7}$

2 Mrs. Lewis baked a tamale pie for the family's dinner. She cut the pie into ten equal pieces. The family ate $\frac{9}{10}$ of the tamale pie as shown by the shaded part of the model.

Which sum is **NOT** equal to $\frac{9}{10}$?

Ⓕ $\frac{2}{10} + \frac{2}{10} + \frac{2}{10} + \frac{1}{10}$

Ⓖ $\frac{2}{10} + \frac{2}{10} + \frac{2}{10} + \frac{3}{10}$

Ⓗ $\frac{4}{10} + \frac{2}{10} + \frac{3}{10}$

Ⓙ $\frac{3}{10} + \frac{3}{10} + \frac{3}{10}$

3 Joseph has 5 chores to complete each day. His mother records this expression to show the part of the chores Joseph completed for 5 days.

$$\frac{4}{5} + \frac{5}{5} + \frac{4}{5} + \frac{3}{5} + \frac{2}{5}$$

Which model correctly represents Joseph's completed chores?

Ⓐ

Ⓑ

Ⓒ

Ⓓ

4 DeAndre uses $1\frac{7}{8}$ cups of rice when he helps his mom prepare dinner. Which expression does **NOT** represent a sum of $1\frac{7}{8}$?

Ⓕ $\frac{8}{8} + \frac{2}{8} + \frac{2}{8} + \frac{2}{8} + \frac{1}{8}$

Ⓖ $1 + \frac{1}{8} + \frac{1}{8} + \frac{1}{8} + \frac{1}{8} + \frac{1}{8} + \frac{1}{8} + \frac{1}{8}$

Ⓗ $\frac{8}{8} + \frac{1}{8} + \frac{1}{8} + \frac{1}{8} + \frac{1}{8} + \frac{2}{8} + \frac{1}{8} + \frac{1}{8}$

Ⓙ $\frac{2}{8} + \frac{2}{8} + \frac{2}{8} + \frac{2}{8} + \frac{2}{8} + \frac{2}{8} + \frac{2}{8} + \frac{1}{8}$

1 Cassie made fruit punch. She mixed $\frac{2}{3}$ cup cherry juice, $\frac{1}{3}$ cup grape juice, $\frac{2}{3}$ cup ginger ale, and $\frac{1}{3}$ cup lime juice. Which fraction equation can be used to find the amount of punch Cassie made?

Cherry Juice   Grape Juice

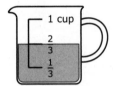

Ginger Ale   Lime Juice

Ⓐ $6 = 2 + 1 + 2 + 1$

Ⓑ $\frac{5}{3} = \frac{1}{3} + \frac{1}{3} + \frac{1}{3} + \frac{1}{3} + \frac{1}{3}$

Ⓒ $\frac{6}{12} = \frac{2}{3} + \frac{1}{3} + \frac{2}{3} + \frac{1}{3}$

Ⓓ $\frac{6}{3} = \frac{2}{3} + \frac{1}{3} + \frac{2}{3} + \frac{1}{3}$

2 Graham wants to give $\frac{7}{10}$ of his Legos® to two friends. Which fraction model does **NOT** show how Graham could divide the Legos® between his two friends?

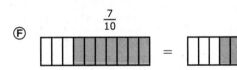

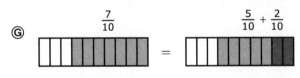

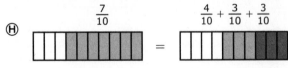

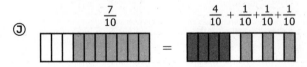

3 Ms. Jefferson's nutty coconut candy recipe uses $\frac{1}{2}$ cup each of chopped pecans and walnuts and $\frac{1}{2}$ cup coconut. Which equation represents the total amount of nuts and coconut Ms. Jefferson uses in her recipe?

Ⓐ $\frac{1}{2} + \frac{1}{2} + \frac{1}{2} = \frac{3}{2} = 1\frac{1}{2}$

Ⓑ $\frac{2}{1} + \frac{2}{1} + \frac{2}{1} = \frac{3}{1} = 3$

Ⓒ $\frac{1}{2} + \frac{1}{2} + \frac{1}{2} = \frac{3}{6}$

Ⓓ $\frac{1}{2} + \frac{1}{2} = \frac{2}{2} = 1$

4 Maya has 15 tickets for rides at the county fair. She gives 3 tickets to her sister. She shares the remaining tickets equally with 2 friends.

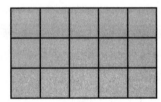

Which represents the fraction of tickets Maya shares with her friends?

Ⓕ $\frac{15}{15} = \frac{3}{15} + \frac{4}{15} + \frac{4}{15} + \frac{4}{15}$

Ⓖ $\frac{15}{15} = \frac{5}{15} + \frac{5}{15} + \frac{5}{15}$

Ⓗ $\frac{3}{15} = \frac{1}{5} + \frac{1}{5} + \frac{1}{5}$

Ⓙ $\frac{12}{15} = \frac{4}{15} + \frac{4}{15} + \frac{4}{15}$

           motivation**math**™ LEVEL 4

1 Lon created a fraction pattern using the rule, "Add the fraction to itself." Lon's fraction pattern is shown below.

$$\frac{\square}{\square}, \ \frac{2}{12}, \ \frac{4}{12}, \ \frac{8}{12}, \ \frac{\square}{\square}$$

What is the first fraction in Lon's pattern?

Answer: _____

What is the last fraction in Lon's pattern?

Answer: _____

Write and solve an equation to find the sum of the 5 fractions in Lon's fraction pattern.

Answer: _____

2 Denise drew a triangle with a total perimeter of 1 foot. Denise's triangle is shown below.

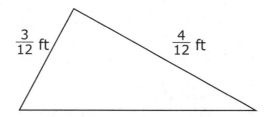

What is the missing measure of the third side of Denise's triangle? _____

Explain how you found your answer. _____

_____

_____

_____

Journal

Serena solves the problem $\frac{3}{5} + \frac{4}{5}$. She says that the sum is $\frac{7}{10}$. Use words and pictorial models to explain why Serena's answer is incorrect.

_____

_____

_____

_____

Vocabulary Activity

Word Box

compose	fraction	unit fraction
decompose	numerator	whole number
denominator		

Select three words from the word box. Write each word on the **KWL** chart. Write what you **K**now about the words in the **K** column. Write what you **W**ant to know about the words in the **W** column. After you have completed the math activities in this unit, write what you **L**earned about the words in the **L** column.

Word	K	W	L

motivation**math**™LEVEL 4
©2014 mentoring**minds**.com

Motivation Mike says, "Go to the head of the class!"

Use these blocks from a set of pattern blocks to help answer the questions.

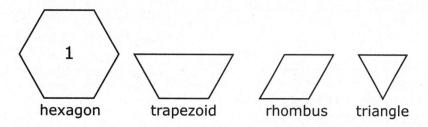

hexagon   trapezoid   rhombus   triangle

If the hexagon is equal to 1, what is the value of the triangle? _____

Use the value of the triangle from the question above. What fraction shows the value of:

the rhombus = _____   the trapezoid = _____

Record the values for the triangle, rhombus, and trapezoid in the empty shapes to decompose the value of each hexagon.

1 = △ + △ + △ + △ + △ + △

1 = △ + △ + △ + △ + ▱

1 = △ + △ + △ + ⬭

1 = ⬭ + ▱ + △

Unit 9 Homework

1 Divide the rectangle below into six equal sections. Decorate some sections with stripes and some with stars.

What fraction represents the total part of the rectangle that has decorated sections?

Answer: _____

Write an equation that represents the sum of the decorated sections.

Answer: _____

2 Draw a picture to illustrate the fraction $\frac{9}{5}$.

Write 2 different equations with a sum of $\frac{9}{5}$.

Answers: _____

_____

3 Lilli uses 3 colors of ribbon to make hair bows. She uses $\frac{3}{4}$ yard of red ribbon, $\frac{2}{4}$ yard of green ribbon, and $\frac{3}{4}$ yard of purple ribbon. Use crayons to create a model for each color of ribbon.

Red ribbon   1 yard

Green ribbon   1 yard

Purple ribbon   1 yard

Write an expression that shows the sum of the shaded models.

Answer: _____

How much ribbon does Lilli use in all?

Answer: _____

Parent Activities

1. Help your child understand fractions by engaging in fraction conversations at mealtime. Ask questions that require your child to add fractions representing the same size parts (e.g., "How many equal parts are there in one whole pizza? How many parts did you eat? How many parts did your brother eat? What fractional part of the whole pizza was eaten?").

2. Give your child a $\frac{1}{4}$-cup measuring cup. Use the cup to measure water in $\frac{1}{4}$-cup measures, each time pouring into a larger (e.g., 1 cup or 2 cup) measuring cup. Discuss how many $\frac{1}{4}$ cups are in 1 cup, or how many $\frac{1}{4}$-cup measures make a total of $\frac{7}{4}$. Repeat with other measures (e.g., thirds, eighths, etc.).

 motivation**math**™ LEVEL 4

1 What fraction is shown by the shaded portion of the figure below?

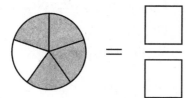

Multiply the numerator and the denominator by 3 to create an equivalent fraction.

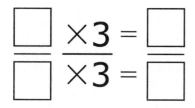

2 Jennifer told her brother that she ran $\frac{3}{5}$ mile after school. Ryan said, "I ran $\frac{5}{8}$ mile, so we ran exactly the same distance." Is Ryan correct? Use the number lines to justify your answer.

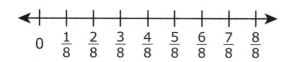

Answer: _____

_____

_____

3 Write two equivalent fractions that name the shaded part of the octagon.

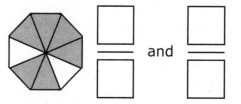

and

4 Which 2 figures show equivalent fractions?

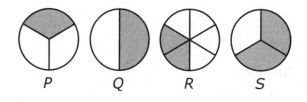

Answer: _____

What 2 equivalent fractions are shown?

Answer: _____

The circle below has been divided into ninths. Shade another fraction that is equivalent to the fractions you named above. What fraction did you shade?

5 Write a number in each box to form equivalent fractions.

$$\frac{2}{5} = \frac{\square}{10} \qquad \frac{2}{3} = \frac{\square}{18}$$

$$\frac{4}{12} = \frac{1}{\square} \qquad \frac{9}{18} = \frac{3}{\square}$$

Use the equivalent fraction chart to answer questions 1–3.

1											
$\frac{1}{2}$						$\frac{1}{2}$					
$\frac{1}{3}$				$\frac{1}{3}$				$\frac{1}{3}$			
$\frac{1}{4}$			$\frac{1}{4}$			$\frac{1}{4}$			$\frac{1}{4}$		
$\frac{1}{5}$		$\frac{1}{5}$		$\frac{1}{5}$		$\frac{1}{5}$		$\frac{1}{5}$			
$\frac{1}{6}$	$\frac{1}{6}$		$\frac{1}{6}$		$\frac{1}{6}$		$\frac{1}{6}$		$\frac{1}{6}$		
$\frac{1}{8}$	$\frac{1}{8}$	$\frac{1}{8}$	$\frac{1}{8}$	$\frac{1}{8}$	$\frac{1}{8}$	$\frac{1}{8}$	$\frac{1}{8}$				
$\frac{1}{9}$	$\frac{1}{9}$	$\frac{1}{9}$	$\frac{1}{9}$	$\frac{1}{9}$	$\frac{1}{9}$	$\frac{1}{9}$	$\frac{1}{9}$	$\frac{1}{9}$			
$\frac{1}{12}$	$\frac{1}{12}$	$\frac{1}{12}$	$\frac{1}{12}$	$\frac{1}{12}$	$\frac{1}{12}$	$\frac{1}{12}$	$\frac{1}{12}$	$\frac{1}{12}$	$\frac{1}{12}$	$\frac{1}{12}$	$\frac{1}{12}$

1 According to the equivalent fraction chart, which fraction is **NOT** equivalent to $\frac{2}{3}$?

Ⓐ $\frac{4}{6}$ Ⓒ $\frac{5}{8}$

Ⓑ $\frac{6}{9}$ Ⓓ $\frac{8}{12}$

2 Marquis needs to name all the fractions shown on the chart that are equivalent to $\frac{1}{2}$. Which list shows these fractions?

Ⓕ $\frac{2}{4}, \frac{3}{6}, \frac{5}{9}, \frac{6}{12}$

Ⓖ $\frac{2}{4}, \frac{3}{6}, \frac{4}{8}$

Ⓗ $\frac{3}{6}, \frac{6}{12}$

Ⓙ $\frac{2}{4}, \frac{3}{6}, \frac{4}{8}, \frac{6}{12}$

3 Which row of fractions in the fraction chart has no equivalent fractions shown?

Ⓐ The row of thirds

Ⓑ The row of fifths

Ⓒ The row of sixths

Ⓓ The row of ninths

4 Shelly has 4 different lengths of hair clips. She wants to wear a clip with a length equivalent to $\frac{14}{16}$ inch. Which length clip should Shelly choose?

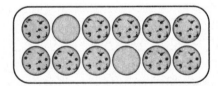

Ⓕ $\frac{3}{4}$ in.   Ⓗ $\frac{7}{8}$ in.

Ⓖ $\frac{6}{8}$ in.   Ⓙ $\frac{1}{2}$ in.

5 Ms. Ewert told her class that $\frac{1}{3}$ of the students in the classroom scored 100 on the math test. There are 24 students in the class. Lisa knew that she could multiply both the numerator and the denominator of the fraction by the same number to find a fraction equivalent to $\frac{1}{3}$. Which number should Lisa use to find the equivalent fraction?

$$\frac{1}{3} = \frac{\square}{24}$$

Ⓐ 12   Ⓒ 6

Ⓑ 8   Ⓓ 4

6 Jess baked cookies for his soccer team. He placed chocolate chips in $\frac{10}{12}$ of the cookies.

Which fraction is equivalent to $\frac{10}{12}$?

Ⓕ $\frac{5}{6}$ Ⓗ $\frac{3}{4}$

Ⓖ $\frac{4}{6}$ Ⓙ $\frac{2}{3}$

1 Which 2 fractions are equivalent to the shaded part of the circle?

Ⓐ $\frac{2}{4}$ and $\frac{1}{2}$

Ⓑ $\frac{1}{3}$ and $\frac{4}{12}$

Ⓒ $\frac{4}{6}$ and $\frac{2}{3}$

Ⓓ $\frac{3}{9}$ and $\frac{1}{3}$

2 Marco made this array of pennies.

Which arrangement should Marco use to show a fraction equivalent to the fraction of pennies that are tails side up?

Ⓕ

Ⓖ

Ⓗ

Ⓙ

3 Jackie uses a ruler to measure the length of a paper clip. She reports the length as $\frac{10}{16}$ inch.

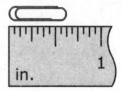

Jackie's teacher asks her to record this length as an equivalent fraction with a denominator of 8. Which fraction should Jackie write?

Ⓐ $\frac{4}{8}$ Ⓒ $\frac{6}{8}$

Ⓑ $\frac{5}{8}$ Ⓓ $\frac{7}{8}$

4 The number lines show fourths and fifths. Both number lines have points marked with letters.

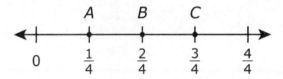

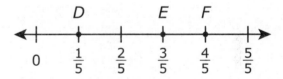

Which statement about the points on the number lines is true?

Ⓕ Points *A* and *D* represent equivalent fractions.

Ⓖ Points *B* and *E* represent equivalent fractions.

Ⓗ Points *C* and *F* represent equivalent fractions.

Ⓙ None of the labeled points on the number lines represents equivalent fractions.

Unit 10 Assessment

1 The pictures below are models of equivalent fractions.

Which represents another fraction that is equivalent to these fractions?

Ⓐ $\frac{1}{4}$ Ⓒ $\frac{6}{12}$

Ⓑ $\frac{2}{5}$ Ⓓ $\frac{5}{9}$

2 Jackson recorded the first four multiples of 5 on a strip of paper and the first four multiples of 6 on another strip of paper. He used a craft stick to create an equivalent fraction model.

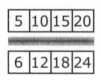

Which is the next fraction equivalent to $\frac{5}{6}$ after $\frac{20}{24}$?

Ⓕ $\frac{21}{25}$ Ⓗ $\frac{25}{28}$

Ⓖ $\frac{24}{27}$ Ⓙ $\frac{25}{30}$

3 Tina knows she can find an equivalent fraction by multiplying OR dividing the numerator and the denominator by the same number. Tina finds 2 fractions that are equivalent to $\frac{9}{15}$. Which fraction pair does Tina find?

Ⓐ $\frac{4}{5}$ and $\frac{20}{25}$ Ⓒ $\frac{2}{5}$ and $\frac{12}{18}$

Ⓑ $\frac{1}{3}$ and $\frac{12}{20}$ Ⓓ $\frac{3}{5}$ and $\frac{18}{30}$

4 The number lines show eighths and twelfths.

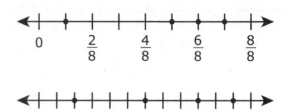

These number lines show that —

Ⓕ $\frac{5}{8}$ is equivalent to $\frac{6}{12}$

Ⓖ $\frac{6}{8}$ is equivalent to $\frac{9}{12}$

Ⓗ $\frac{1}{8}$ is equivalent to $\frac{2}{12}$

Ⓙ $\frac{7}{8}$ is equivalent to $\frac{11}{12}$

5 Carl worked with equivalent fractions in his math class. He discovered that $\frac{1}{3}$ is equivalent to $\frac{4}{12}$. What is one way Carl might have determined this?

Ⓐ He added the numerator and the denominator in $\frac{1}{3}$ to find the 4 in $\frac{4}{12}$.

Ⓑ He multiplied 4 × 1 and 6 × 2 to find the equivalent fraction $\frac{4}{12}$.

Ⓒ He multiplied $\frac{1}{3}$ by $\frac{4}{4}$ to find the equivalent fraction $\frac{4}{12}$.

Ⓓ He divided the numerator of $\frac{1}{3}$ by 1 and the denominator by 4 to find that $\frac{4}{12}$ is equivalent to $\frac{1}{3}$.

 motivationmath™LEVEL 4 ©2014 mentoring**minds**.com

1 Joni's jar of 10 marbles contains red, blue, and yellow marbles, as shown in this picture. How many red marbles would Joni need to add to the jar so that $\frac{1}{3}$ of the marbles are red?

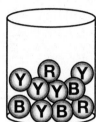

Answer: _____

Explain why you selected this number.

_____

_____

_____

_____

2 Tommy, Felipe, and Matthew each brought 1 sandwich for lunch. Each boy ate half of his sandwich and saved the other half to eat after recess. Tommy ate only 1 piece. Felipe ate 2 pieces, and Matthew ate 4 pieces. The sandwiches were the same size, and each boy ate an equivalent amount. Draw lines on the sandwiches to show how each was cut. Color the parts of the sandwiches that the boys ate.

Tommy's Sandwich   Felipe's Sandwich   Matthew's Sandwich

Explain your thinking.

_____

_____

_____

Unit 10 Journal/Vocabulary Activity

Journal

Jon and Sebastian measured the length of a line segment with an inch ruler. Jon reported the length as $\frac{3}{4}$ inch long. Sebastian said the length was $\frac{12}{16}$ inch long.

The teacher said that both boys were correct. Explain how this is possible.

_____

_____

_____

Vocabulary Activity

Three words are written in each row below. For each row, circle the word that does **NOT** belong. Then explain why that word does not belong with the others.

1. denominator   numerator   decimal

_____

2. equal   fraction   equivalent

_____

3. part   whole   piece

_____

4. addition   multiplication   division

_____

Motivation Molly says, "You're in touch with math!"

Fraction Spin

Use a pencil and paper clip with the spinners to play *Fraction Spin* with a partner. Each player needs a game sheet. The first player spins Spinner 1 to find the numerator of a fraction. The second player spins Spinner 2 to find the denominator of the fraction. Both players record the fraction in the space provided on their separate game sheets and then write 3 additional fractions that are equivalent to the fraction created with the spinners.

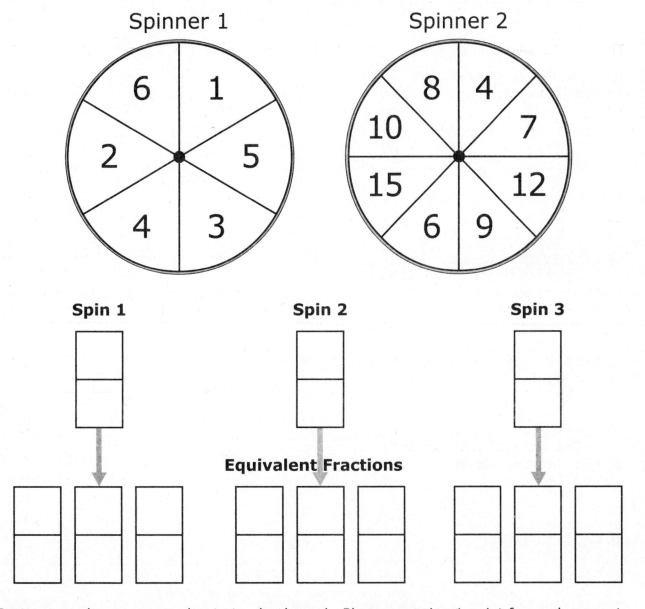

Partners exchange game sheets to check work. Players receive 1 point for each correct equivalent fraction. The player with the highest score wins.

Variation: Score 1 bonus point for each equivalent fraction that is different from your partner's equivalent fractions.

Unit 10 Homework

1 The first rectangle has been partitioned into thirds. Shade and label $\frac{1}{3}$ of the rectangle. Then partition, shade, and label the other two rectangles to show fractions that are equivalent to $\frac{1}{3}$.

_____   _____   _____

What patterns do you see in these equivalent fractions?

_____

_____

2 Lizzy drew this number line and labeled Point *A*.

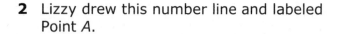

Name two equivalent fractions that are represented by Point *A* on Lizzy's number line.

Answer: _____

Locate and label another pair of equivalent fractions that may be shown on Lizzy's number line.

3 Juan helped his mother in the kitchen. He said, "I can show equivalent fractions on this measuring cup."

Explain what Juan meant.

_____

_____

_____

_____

4 In the space below, draw a model that shows that $\frac{6}{8} = \frac{3}{4}$.

Parent Activities

1. Let your child experiment with measuring cups. Measure to see how many $\frac{1}{4}$ cups of rice equal $\frac{1}{2}$ cup and how many equal 1 cup. Repeat to see how many $\frac{1}{3}$ cups of rice equal $\frac{2}{3}$ cup and 1 cup.

2. Talk about the letters in family members' names. Write the fractional parts of vowels and consonants for each name. Then name two fractions that are equivalent to these fractions (e.g., In the name Daniel, $\frac{3}{6}$ of the letters are vowels. Equivalent fractions include $\frac{1}{2}$ and $\frac{6}{12}$.).

 motivation**math**™LEVEL 4

1 Use the following 6 fractions to create 3 true comparisons using >, <, and = . Each fraction may be used only one time. Draw models to support each comparison.

$$\frac{1}{2} \qquad \frac{2}{6} \qquad \frac{2}{3} \qquad \frac{4}{8} \qquad \frac{3}{4} \qquad \frac{3}{10}$$

$\dfrac{\square}{\square} > \dfrac{\square}{\square}$ $\qquad$ $\dfrac{\square}{\square} < \dfrac{\square}{\square}$ $\qquad$ $\dfrac{\square}{\square} = \dfrac{\square}{\square}$

2 Carlton uses fraction bars to compare fractions. Label the fraction bars. List the fractions shown on the fraction bars that are greater than $\frac{1}{4}$ but less than $\frac{3}{4}$.

_____

_____

_____

1			
$\frac{1}{2}$		$\frac{1}{2}$	
$\frac{1}{3}$			

How can fraction bars help compare fractions?

_____

_____

_____

Unit 11 Journal/Vocabulary Activity

Journal

Circle the larger fraction.

$$\frac{3}{8} \qquad \text{or} \qquad \frac{4}{6}$$

Explain how you determined the answer.

_____

_____

_____

_____

Vocabulary Activity

Use the fractions to answer the questions below. You may use a fraction more than once.

$$\frac{1}{4} \qquad \frac{2}{3} \qquad \frac{3}{5} \qquad \frac{8}{8} \qquad \frac{6}{12} \qquad \frac{2}{6} \qquad \frac{6}{10} \qquad \frac{2}{8}$$

1. Which pair of fractions makes this number sentence true? _____ = _____

2. Circle all the fractions greater than $\frac{1}{2}$.

3. Draw a box around all the fractions less than $\frac{1}{2}$.

4. Which fraction has a value equal to 1? _____

5. Which fractions make this comparison true? $\frac{3}{5} <$ _____

6. Which fraction makes this comparison true? _____ $> \frac{2}{3}$

7. Which fractions have the same numerators? _____

motivation**math**™ LEVEL 4
©2014 mentoring**minds**.com

 **Motivation Mike says,** "This is top-notch work!"

Fraction Action

Play *Fraction Action* with a partner. Each pair needs a game board and a pencil and paper clip for the spinner. Each player needs a different color crayon. Player 1 spins the spinner and colors the correct number of triangles according to the following.

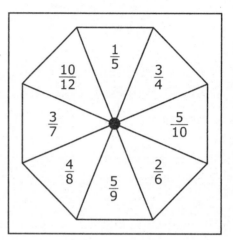

- If the spinner lands on a fraction less than $\frac{1}{2}$, the player colors 1 triangle.

- If the spinner lands on a fraction greater than $\frac{1}{2}$, the player colors 2 triangles.

- If the spinner lands on a fraction equal to $\frac{1}{2}$, the player colors 3 triangles.

When all triangles have been colored, the winner is the player with the most colored triangles.

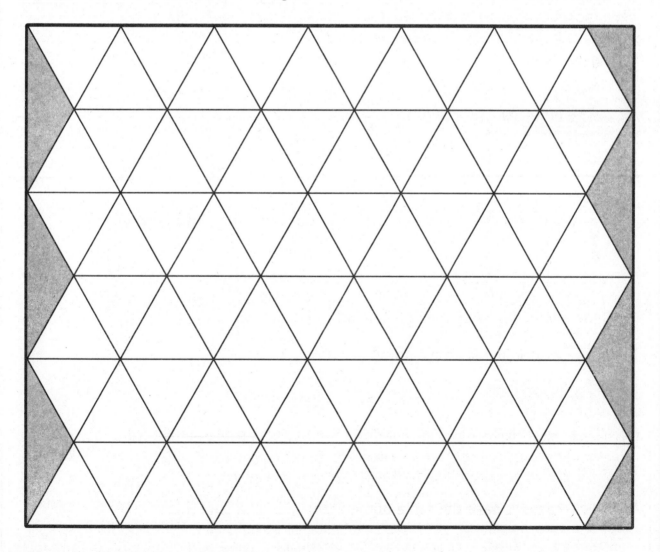

1 Study the fraction comparison below.

$$\frac{4}{6} = \frac{?}{12}$$

What numerator makes this comparison number sentence true?

Answer: _____

2 Rachel made a pan of veggie lasagna and a pan of meat lasagna. She cut each pan into 16 equal servings. Twelve-sixteenths of the veggie lasagna was eaten, and $\frac{3}{4}$ of the meat lasagna was eaten. Draw lines and shade the models below to represent the amounts of lasagna eaten. Then complete the number sentence.

Veggie Lasagna   Meat Lasagna

$$\frac{\square}{\square} \bigcirc \frac{\square}{\square}$$

3 Mallory and Grace each need 1 yard of fabric for a project. Mallory has $\frac{5}{8}$ yard, and Grace has $\frac{2}{3}$ yard. Shade the models below to show the fabric each girl has.

Mallory's Fabric

Grace's Fabric

Who needs more fabric to complete the project?

Answer: _____

Explain your answer.

_____

_____

_____

_____

Complete each fraction comparison.

4 Write >, <, or = in the circles.

$$\frac{3}{5} \bigcirc \frac{6}{15} \qquad \frac{5}{21} \bigcirc \frac{2}{7}$$

Parent Activities

1. Help your child compare two fractional quantities by asking questions about real-world situations (e.g., "I have eaten $\frac{1}{2}$ of my sandwich, and you have eaten $\frac{1}{4}$ of your sandwich. How do these fractions compare?").

2. When your family orders pizza, discuss fractional parts of the pizza. Talk about which family member eats the greatest or the smallest fractional part. Ask questions such as, "The pizza is cut into 8 equal slices. Which is larger, $\frac{1}{2}$ or $\frac{3}{8}$? What fractional part of the pizza is equal to $\frac{1}{2}$?"

1 What is $\frac{2}{6} + \frac{3}{6}$?

Answer: _____

Draw a model to represent your answer.

2 Alli used a number line to solve a fraction word problem.

Miguel drives $2\frac{1}{4}$ miles from work to the gas station. He must drive $3\frac{2}{4}$ additional miles to get home. How far does Miguel drive from work to his home?

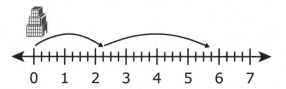

Samah also used a number line to solve the same problem by adding the whole numbers and then the fractions. Use the number line below to show Samah's work.

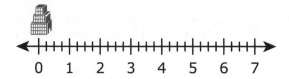

Does Samah find the same answer as Alli?

Answer: _____

Explain your thinking.

_____

_____

_____

3 Before Lydia's birthday party, $4\frac{1}{8}$ pages of her sticker book were full. After the party, Lydia filled an additional $2\frac{4}{8}$ pages. Shade the model to represent Lydia's sticker book.

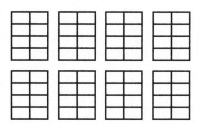

How many pages has Lydia filled?

Answer: _____

4 On Saturday, Nancy and Michelle jogged in the park. The strip diagram below shows the distance each girl jogged.

Nancy

$\frac{8}{10}$ mile

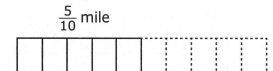

Michelle

$\frac{5}{10}$ mile

How much farther did Nancy jog than Michelle?

Answer: _____

⭐ **Unit 12** Guided Practice

1 Which number line best represents $\frac{6}{8} + \frac{3}{8}$?

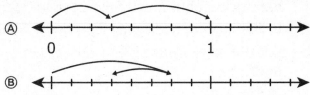

2 Antonio has the quarters shown below.

He pays $0.75 for a package of bubble gum at the convenience store. What fraction of Antonio's quarters are left?

Ⓕ $\frac{3}{9}$ Ⓗ $\frac{6}{9}$

Ⓖ $\frac{2}{9}$ Ⓙ $\frac{5}{9}$

3 Katherine gave $\frac{2}{12}$ of her candy bar to her cousin and $\frac{3}{12}$ of the candy bar to her brother.

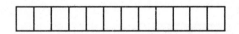

Which shows how much of the candy bar Katherine gave away?

Ⓐ $\frac{5}{12}$ Ⓒ $\frac{1}{12}$

Ⓑ $\frac{6}{12}$ Ⓓ $\frac{7}{12}$

4 Erica and Jose order a medium pepperoni pizza from Bruno's Pizza Parlor. Erica eats 2 slices of pizza, and Jose eats 4 slices.

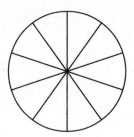

If the pizza had a total of 10 slices, which fraction represents the amount of pizza **NOT** eaten?

Ⓕ $\frac{6}{10}$

Ⓖ $\frac{5}{10}$

Ⓗ $\frac{2}{10}$

Ⓙ $\frac{4}{10}$

5 Chloe painted her bedroom with paint she found in the garage. She found $3\frac{5}{8}$ gallons. She used $2\frac{2}{8}$ gallons.

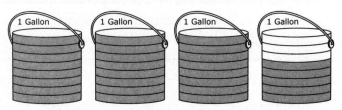

Which equation can be used to find how much paint was left after Chloe finished painting?

Ⓐ $3\frac{5}{8} - 2\frac{2}{8} = 1\frac{3}{8}$

Ⓑ $3\frac{5}{8} - 2\frac{2}{8} = 1\frac{7}{8}$

Ⓒ $3\frac{5}{8} + 2\frac{2}{8} = 5\frac{3}{8}$

Ⓓ $3\frac{2}{8} + 2\frac{5}{8} = 5\frac{7}{8}$

motivation**math**™ LEVEL 4

1 Destiny and Trina purchased a small cheesecake from McGraw's Bakery. Destiny ate $\frac{3}{6}$ of the cheesecake, and Trina ate $\frac{1}{6}$. Which shows the fraction of the cheesecake Destiny and Trina had left?

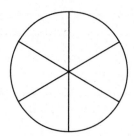

Ⓐ $\frac{4}{6}$ Ⓒ $\frac{1}{6}$

Ⓑ $\frac{2}{3}$ Ⓓ $\frac{2}{6}$

2 Marcy runs $1\frac{4}{5}$ miles on Monday, $2\frac{1}{5}$ miles on Tuesday, and $1\frac{2}{5}$ miles on Wednesday. She uses a number line to record her running record. Which number line does **NOT** represent Marcy's run?

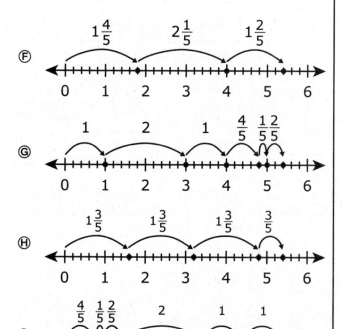

3 Sarah's mother wants to bake a cake. Her recipe calls for $1\frac{2}{4}$ cups brown sugar and $\frac{3}{4}$ cup white sugar.

Brown Sugar   White Sugar

What is the total amount of sugar required for the cake recipe?

Ⓐ $1\frac{2}{4} + \frac{3}{4} = 2\frac{1}{4}$ cups

Ⓑ $1\frac{2}{4} + \frac{3}{4} = 3\frac{1}{4}$ cups

Ⓒ $1\frac{2}{4} - \frac{3}{4} = \frac{3}{4}$ cup

Ⓓ $1\frac{2}{4} - \frac{2}{4} = 1$ cup

4 The table shows the number of flowers in an arrangement of a dozen flowers.

Flower Arrangement

Type of Flower	Number
Rose	4
Daisy	5
Carnation	3

Which shaded model shows the fraction of flowers in the arrangement that are roses and carnations?

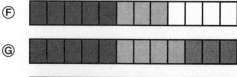

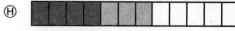

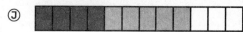

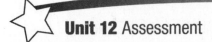
1 Carson and Savannah make peanut butter cookies. The recipe calls for $1\frac{3}{8}$ cup of butter and $\frac{5}{8}$ cup of peanut butter. How much more butter is needed than peanut butter?

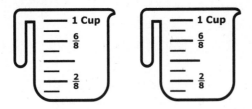

Ⓐ $1\frac{3}{8} + \frac{5}{8} = 1\frac{8}{8} = 2$ cups

Ⓑ $1\frac{3}{8} - \frac{5}{8} = \frac{5}{8}$ cup

Ⓒ $1\frac{3}{8} - \frac{5}{8} = \frac{6}{8}$ cup

Ⓓ $1\frac{3}{8} + \frac{5}{8} = 2\frac{4}{8}$ cups

2 Billy and Jason raked leaves in the backyard. They had ten trash bags for bagging the leaves. Billy used $\frac{2}{10}$ of the bags. Jason used $\frac{3}{10}$ of the bags. Later their friend Michael came over to help. He used $\frac{2}{10}$ of the bags. What fraction of the bags were **NOT** used?

Ⓕ $\frac{7}{10}$ of the bags

Ⓖ $\frac{5}{10}$ of the bags

Ⓗ $\frac{4}{10}$ of the bags

Ⓙ $\frac{3}{10}$ of the bags

3 Elizabeth records the time she spends reading a library book. She reads for $\frac{3}{4}$ hour before school, $\frac{1}{4}$ hour during silent reading time in class, and $1\frac{2}{4}$ hours after dinner. Which number line shows the total time Elizabeth spent reading?

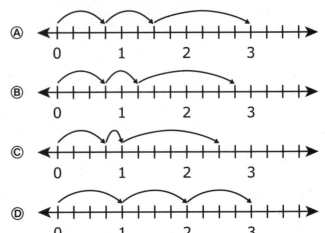

4 The table shows the number of coins in Amanda's wallet.

Amanda's Wallet

Coin	Number
Penny	6
Nickel	1
Dime	3
Quarter	5

Which equation can be used to find the fraction of coins in Amanda's wallet that are pennies or dimes?

Ⓕ $\frac{6}{15} + \frac{1}{15} = \frac{7}{15}$

Ⓖ $\frac{1}{15} + \frac{5}{15} = \frac{6}{15}$

Ⓗ $\frac{3}{15} + \frac{5}{15} = \frac{8}{15}$

Ⓙ $\frac{6}{15} + \frac{3}{15} = \frac{9}{15}$

motivation**math**™ LEVEL 4

Name _____

1 Maggie helped her mom paint the fence. The fence has 8 sections, and each section has 4 boards. Maggie and her mom painted $2\frac{1}{4}$ sections of fence on Monday. On Tuesday, they painted $3\frac{1}{4}$ sections of fence. Use different colors to shade the fence sections Maggie and her mom painted on Monday and Tuesday.

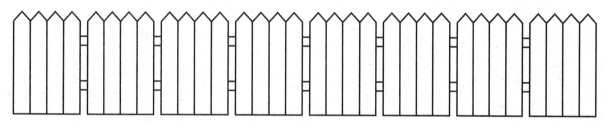

How many sections of fence do they need to paint on Wednesday to complete the job?

Answer: _____

Write two equations that are needed to solve the problem mathematically.

_____

_____

2 Think about the skills and characteristics that allow students to be successful in math. Create a recipe for math success using at least four ingredients. Use fractions and mixed numbers for each of the ingredients (e.g., $2\frac{1}{4}$ cups listening in class).

Recipe for Math Success

Ingredients:

Directions:

Unit 12 Journal/Vocabulary Activity

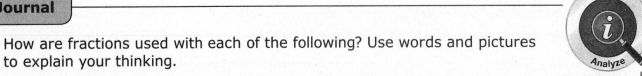

Journal

How are fractions used with each of the following? Use words and pictures to explain your thinking.

Number Line	Ruler	Cooking	Clock

Vocabulary Activity

Analogies show relationships. Some relationships are shown below.

wall : room	a *wall* is part of a *room* — the relationship is part to whole
laugh : cry	*laugh* is the opposite of *cry* — the relationship is an antonym
wrong : incorrect	*wrong* has the same meaning as *incorrect* — the relationship is a synonym

Complete these analogies, and then explain the relationships.

1. add : subtract :: numerator : _____

Explain the relationship shown by the analogy.

_____

2. fraction : _____ :: leaf : tree

Explain the relationship shown by the analogy.

_____

3. peak : mountain :: _____ : fraction

Explain the relationship shown by the analogy.

_____

motivation**math**™LEVEL 4   ©2014 mentoring**minds**.com

Motivation Molly says, "You're incredible!"

Fraction Quilt

Play *Fraction Quilt* with a friend. Each player needs a game board and colored pencils. Using a paper clip and pencil, player 1 spins the spinner. Player 1 colors in the fraction of quilt pieces equal to the fraction shown on the spinner. Each row of the quilt is divided into different fractions. If the player spins $\frac{2}{8}$, the player colors in 2 parts of the row with 8 equal sections or 1 section of the row with 4 equal sections, since $\frac{2}{8} = \frac{1}{4}$. If there are not enough blank squares to color the fraction spun, the player skips a turn. Play alternates between partners. The winner is the first person to complete the quilt.

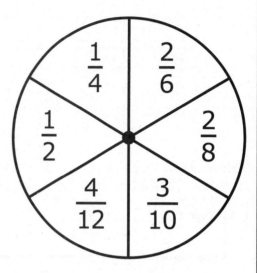

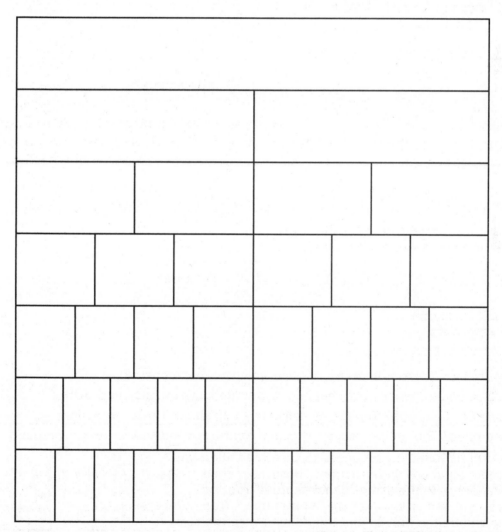

1 Alberto made punch using $2\frac{3}{4}$ cups of apple juice, $1\frac{1}{4}$ cups of pineapple juice, and $1\frac{1}{4}$ cups of water.

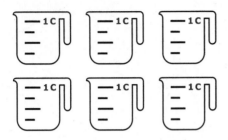

How many cups of punch did Alberto make? Shade the cups to solve.

Answer: _____

2 Audra needs $1\frac{6}{8}$ yards of fabric to make an apron. She has $\frac{7}{8}$ yard of fabric. Her aunt gives her $\frac{3}{8}$ yard. Draw a strip diagram to show the fabric Audra has now.

Does Audra have enough fabric to make the apron?

Answer: _____

What is the difference between the fabric Audra has and the amount she needs?

Answer: _____

Use the map to answer questions 3 and 4.

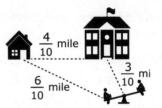

Leslie walks $\frac{4}{10}$ mile from her house to school. After school Leslie goes to a park that is $\frac{3}{10}$ mile from the school. She then walks home, a distance of $\frac{6}{10}$ mile.

3 Draw a number line to find the total distance Leslie walks.

How far does Leslie walk?

Answer: _____

4 Create a strip diagram to find how much farther Leslie walks from the park to her house than she walks from school to the park.

Answer: _____

Parent Activities

1. Allow your child to assist in measuring ingredients when cooking. Ask questions such as, "What would happen to the amounts of each ingredient if we doubled the recipe? The recipe calls for $\frac{3}{4}$ cup sugar. How much sugar would we need? The recipe calls for $\frac{3}{8}$ cup of flour. How much flour would we use?"

2. Use a set of double-nine dominoes to create addition and subtraction equations with fractions. Have your child choose two dominoes with the same "denominators" (bottom numbers) and add or subtract the "numerators" (top numbers). See who can be the first to find the domino with the correct fraction sum or difference.

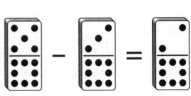

Use the chart to answer questions 1–4.

Knowing which fractions are close to $\frac{1}{2}$ or 1 helps determine the reasonableness of sums and differences. Study the fraction bars on the chart below.

1 whole											
$\frac{1}{2}$						$\frac{1}{2}$					
$\frac{1}{3}$				$\frac{1}{3}$				$\frac{1}{3}$			
$\frac{1}{4}$			$\frac{1}{4}$			$\frac{1}{4}$			$\frac{1}{4}$		
$\frac{1}{5}$		$\frac{1}{5}$		$\frac{1}{5}$		$\frac{1}{5}$		$\frac{1}{5}$			
$\frac{1}{6}$		$\frac{1}{6}$		$\frac{1}{6}$		$\frac{1}{6}$		$\frac{1}{6}$		$\frac{1}{6}$	
$\frac{1}{8}$	$\frac{1}{8}$	$\frac{1}{8}$	$\frac{1}{8}$	$\frac{1}{8}$	$\frac{1}{8}$	$\frac{1}{8}$	$\frac{1}{8}$				
$\frac{1}{9}$	$\frac{1}{9}$	$\frac{1}{9}$	$\frac{1}{9}$	$\frac{1}{9}$	$\frac{1}{9}$	$\frac{1}{9}$	$\frac{1}{9}$	$\frac{1}{9}$			
$\frac{1}{10}$	$\frac{1}{10}$	$\frac{1}{10}$	$\frac{1}{10}$	$\frac{1}{10}$	$\frac{1}{10}$	$\frac{1}{10}$	$\frac{1}{10}$	$\frac{1}{10}$	$\frac{1}{10}$		
$\frac{1}{12}$	$\frac{1}{12}$	$\frac{1}{12}$	$\frac{1}{12}$	$\frac{1}{12}$	$\frac{1}{12}$	$\frac{1}{12}$	$\frac{1}{12}$	$\frac{1}{12}$	$\frac{1}{12}$	$\frac{1}{12}$	$\frac{1}{12}$

1 Name 3 fractions that are equivalent to $\frac{1}{2}$.

Answers: _____

What pattern do you see in the numerators and denominators of these fractions?

Answer: _____

_____

How can you use this pattern to determine which fractions are less than $\frac{1}{2}$ and which are greater than $\frac{1}{2}$?

Answer: _____

_____

2 Name 3 fractions that are close to 1 whole, but not equivalent to 1 whole.

Answer: _____

What generalization can you make about the numerator and denominator of a fraction that is close to 1?

Answer: _____

_____

What generalization can you make about the numerator and denominator of a fraction that is close to 0?

Answer: _____

_____

3 Alta estimates the sum of $\frac{2}{5}$ and $\frac{4}{9}$. She thinks the sum is greater than 1. Do you agree?

Yes   No

Explain your thinking.

_____

_____

4 Bert has 2 dowel rods. One is $\frac{9}{10}$ foot long, and the other is $\frac{7}{8}$ foot long. Bert says he can glue the rods together to make a rod that is almost 2 feet long. Do you agree?

Yes   No

Explain your thinking.

_____

_____

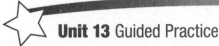
Use the number line to answer questions 1 and 2.

Some benchmark numbers are labeled on the number line below.

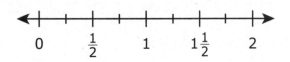

$$0 \quad \frac{1}{2} \quad 1 \quad 1\frac{1}{2} \quad 2$$

1 Joe found a sum of $\frac{2}{6}$ when he added $\frac{1}{4} + \frac{1}{2}$. Is Joe's answer reasonable?

Ⓐ Yes, because $\frac{2}{6}$ is greater than $\frac{1}{2}$

Ⓑ No, because $\frac{2}{6}$ is less than $\frac{1}{2}$

Ⓒ Yes, because $\frac{2}{6}$ is less than 1

Ⓓ No, because the sum should be a fraction between $\frac{1}{4}$ and $\frac{1}{2}$

2 Angie has 2 yards of ribbon. She says, "If I give Amy $\frac{3}{8}$ yard of ribbon, I'll still have a little more than $1\frac{1}{2}$ yards of ribbon left for my craft project." Is Angie's estimate reasonable?

Ⓕ No, $\frac{3}{8}$ is a little more than $\frac{1}{2}$.

Ⓖ No, $\frac{3}{8}$ is closer to 1 than it is to $\frac{1}{2}$.

Ⓗ Yes, $\frac{3}{8}$ is less than $\frac{1}{2}$.

Ⓙ Yes, because Amy will give some of the ribbon back.

3 During track practice, Jay ran $\frac{5}{12}$ mile, while Li ran $\frac{4}{9}$ mile. Which best describes the total distance Jay and Li ran?

Ⓐ Less than 1 mile

Ⓑ Exactly 1 mile

Ⓒ A little more than 1 mile

Ⓓ Less than $\frac{1}{2}$ mile

4 Which of the following has a sum greater than 1?

Ⓕ $\frac{2}{5} + \frac{3}{8}$ Ⓗ $\frac{1}{10} + \frac{5}{12}$

Ⓖ $\frac{3}{7} + \frac{2}{9}$ Ⓙ $\frac{5}{8} + \frac{4}{7}$

5 River needs $1\frac{1}{2}$ cups of sugar to bake his favorite cookies. He finds $\frac{7}{8}$ cup of sugar in the sugar bowl and $\frac{11}{12}$ cup of sugar in a canister in the pantry. Does River have enough sugar to bake his favorite cookies?

Ⓐ No, the fractions $\frac{7}{8}$ and $\frac{11}{12}$ are both close to $\frac{1}{2}$, so River has less than 1 full cup of sugar.

Ⓑ No, the sum of $\frac{7}{8}$ and $\frac{11}{12}$ is $\frac{18}{20}$, which is close to 1.

Ⓒ Yes, the sum of $\frac{7}{8}$ and $\frac{11}{12}$ is close to 1, so River can bake a low-sugar version of the cookie.

Ⓓ Yes, $\frac{7}{8}$ is close to 1 and $\frac{11}{12}$ is close to 1, so River has more than $1\frac{1}{2}$ cups of sugar.

6 Cam's mom told him he could spend $\frac{11}{12}$ hour playing outside before dinner. So far he has spent $\frac{1}{4}$ hour playing outside. Which best describes the fractional part of an hour Cam has left to play outside?

Ⓕ It is greater than 0 but less than $\frac{1}{4}$.

Ⓖ It is greater than $\frac{1}{4}$ but less than $\frac{1}{2}$.

Ⓗ It is greater than $\frac{1}{2}$ but less than $\frac{3}{4}$.

Ⓙ It is greater than $\frac{3}{4}$ but less than 1.

1 Barb purchased 2 candy bars from the band club. She ate $\frac{1}{2}$ of one candy bar. The remaining candy is shaded in the picture below.

Barb gave her sister a piece of candy that was $\frac{3}{7}$ of a whole candy bar. Which is true about the amount of candy Barb has left?

ⓐ Barb has only $\frac{1}{2}$ of a candy bar left.

ⓑ Barb has a little more than 1 whole candy bar left.

ⓒ Barb has no candy left.

ⓓ Barb has $\frac{3}{4}$ of a candy bar left.

2 Rob estimates that the sum of $\frac{7}{8} + \frac{8}{9}$ is close to 1. Is Rob's estimate reasonable?

ⓕ Yes, since $\frac{15}{17}$ is close to 1, the estimate is reasonable.

ⓖ Yes, since $\frac{7}{8}$ and $\frac{8}{9}$ both have values close to $\frac{1}{2}$, the sum will be close to 1.

ⓗ No, the sum must be greater than both addends, and $\frac{8}{9}$ is greater than 1.

ⓙ No, since $\frac{7}{8}$ has a value close to 1 and $\frac{8}{9}$ has a value close to 1, the sum is closer to 2.

3 During the walk-a-thon, Cooper walked $\frac{9}{10}$ kilometer and Mia walked $\frac{3}{5}$ kilometer. Which is the best estimate of their combined distance?

ⓐ About $\frac{1}{2}$ kilometer

ⓑ About 1 kilometer

ⓒ About $1\frac{1}{2}$ kilometers

ⓓ About 2 kilometers

4 On Tuesday, Sofia watched TV for $1\frac{3}{5}$ hours. On Wednesday, she watched TV for $\frac{2}{3}$ hour. Which best describes how long Sofia watched TV?

ⓕ Less than 2 hours

ⓖ Exactly 2 hours

ⓗ A little more than 2 hours

ⓙ A little more than 3 hours

5 Miguel fed his pet rabbits $\frac{5}{6}$ cup of food on Tuesday. He estimated that the rabbits left about $\frac{1}{10}$ cup of food uneaten. Which is a reasonable estimate of the fraction of a cup of food Miguel's rabbits ate on Tuesday?

ⓐ It is greater than 0 but less than $\frac{1}{4}$.

ⓑ It is greater than $\frac{1}{4}$ but less than $\frac{1}{3}$.

ⓒ It is greater than $\frac{1}{3}$ but less than $\frac{1}{2}$.

ⓓ It is greater than $\frac{1}{2}$ but less than 1.

Unit 13 Assessment

1 Nate says that the sum of $\frac{1}{2}$ and $\frac{1}{3}$ is $\frac{2}{5}$. Is Nate's answer reasonable?

Ⓐ Nate's answer is not reasonable because $\frac{2}{5}$ is less than $\frac{1}{2}$.

Ⓑ Nate's answer is reasonable because the sum of two fractions is always another fraction.

Ⓒ Nate's answer is not reasonable because the sum is greater than 1.

Ⓓ Nate's answer is reasonable because the sum is greater than $\frac{1}{3}$.

2 Pete is starting a fitness program which includes running and walking. One afternoon, Pete walked for $\frac{1}{4}$ mile and ran for another $\frac{3}{8}$ mile. Which is the best estimate of the fractional part of a mile Pete traveled altogether?

Ⓕ It is greater than 0 but less than $\frac{3}{8}$.

Ⓖ It is greater than $\frac{3}{8}$ but less than $\frac{1}{2}$.

Ⓗ It is greater than $\frac{1}{2}$ but less than $\frac{3}{4}$.

Ⓙ It is greater than $\frac{3}{4}$ but less than 1.

3 Which of the following has a sum less than 1?

Ⓐ $\frac{9}{10} + \frac{3}{4}$

Ⓑ $\frac{11}{12} + \frac{5}{8}$

Ⓒ $\frac{2}{5} + \frac{3}{7}$

Ⓓ Not here

4 Shirell purchased a package containing $1\frac{3}{8}$ pounds of ground meat. She used $\frac{9}{10}$ pound of the meat to make hamburgers. Which is the most reasonable estimate of the weight of the remaining ground meat?

Ⓕ 0 pounds Ⓗ 1 pound

Ⓖ $\frac{1}{2}$ pound Ⓙ $1\frac{1}{2}$ pounds

5 Helen had 2 small cheese pizzas. Helen gave her brother $\frac{7}{8}$ of one pizza, and she ate all the remaining pizza. Which is closest to how much pizza Helen ate?

Ⓐ $\frac{1}{2}$ pizza Ⓒ 1 pizza

Ⓑ $\frac{3}{4}$ pizza Ⓓ $1\frac{1}{2}$ pizzas

6 Darla's family went on a vacation to Yellowstone Park. On day 1, they drove $\frac{1}{4}$ the total distance, and on day 2 they drove an additional $\frac{1}{5}$ the total distance. Which shows about how far the family has left to travel to Yellowstone Park?

Ⓕ Less than $\frac{1}{4}$ the total distance

Ⓖ More than $\frac{3}{4}$ the total distance

Ⓗ Close to $\frac{1}{2}$ the total distance

Ⓙ Exactly $\frac{3}{4}$ the total distance

 motivation**math**™LEVEL 4 ©2014 mentoring**minds**.com

1 Mrs. Johnson gave Karman this list of fractions.

$$\frac{11}{12} \qquad \frac{5}{12} \qquad \frac{1}{6} \qquad \frac{1}{3} \qquad \frac{3}{4} \qquad \frac{1}{8} \qquad \frac{3}{8} \qquad \frac{5}{8} \qquad \frac{1}{4} \qquad \frac{2}{3}$$

Karman needs to place the fractions in the Venn diagram shown below. Help Karman by writing each fraction in the correct area of the diagram.

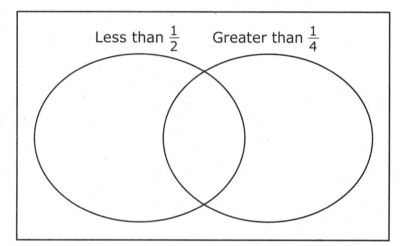

Less than $\frac{1}{2}$ Greater than $\frac{1}{4}$

2 Write an estimation word problem in which the answer is approximately $2\frac{1}{2}$.

_____

_____

_____

_____

_____

Unit 13 Journal/Vocabulary Activity

Journal

How is estimating a sum with fraction addends different from estimating a sum with whole number addends?

_____

_____

_____

_____

_____

Vocabulary Activity

Read the clues to complete the puzzle.

Across

6. an approximate calculation
7. the answer to an addition problem

Down

1. a part of a group or a whole
2. fractions with the same value
3. sensible or logical
4. a point of reference from which measurements or estimates may be made
5. the answer to a subtraction problem

motivation**math**™ LEVEL 4

Motivation Mike says, "Extraordinary work!"

Color Blast

Look at the addition problems in the design below. Use benchmarks to find a reasonable estimate of each sum. Determine if the answer is closest to 0, 1, or 2, and use the directions to color each space.

- If the estimate is closest to 0, color the space yellow.

- If the estimate is closest to 1, color the space red.

- If the estimate is closest to 2, color the space blue.

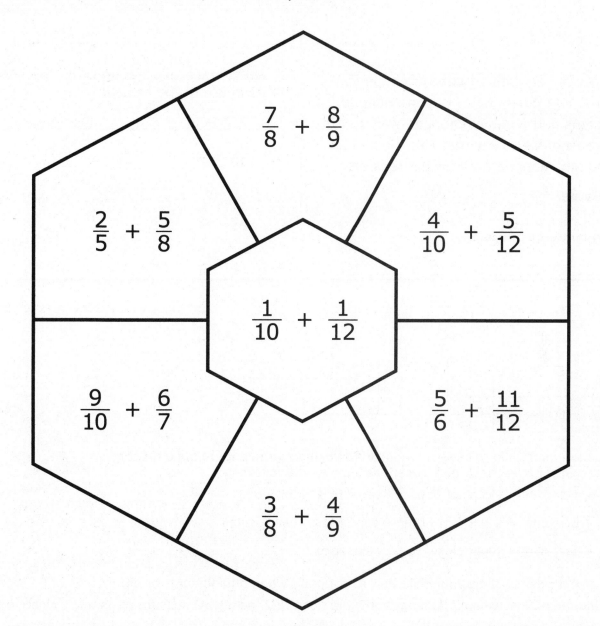

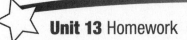

Unit 13 Homework

1 Cecily worked out at the gym for $\frac{11}{12}$ hour on Monday. She worked out for $\frac{5}{6}$ hour on Wednesday. About how many hours did Cecily work out?

Answer: _____

Explain your answer.

_____

_____

2 A recipe requires $1\frac{1}{4}$ cups of chopped nuts. Mrs. Spain has $\frac{3}{4}$ cup of chopped pecans and $\frac{7}{8}$ cup of chopped walnuts. Is it reasonable to say that Mrs. Spain has enough chopped nuts for the recipe?

Answer: _____

Explain your answer.

_____

_____

3 Walter completed $\frac{1}{3}$ of his homework before dinner. He completed $\frac{4}{9}$ of his homework after dinner. Is it reasonable to conclude that Walter has completed all his homework?

Answer: _____

Explain your answer.

_____

_____

4 Match each expression with a reasonable estimate of the answer.

Expression	Estimate
$\frac{9}{10} - \frac{3}{7}$	$1\frac{1}{2}$
$\frac{11}{12} + \frac{8}{9}$	$\frac{1}{2}$
$\frac{5}{8} + \frac{6}{7}$	2
$\frac{4}{9} + \frac{5}{8}$	1

✂ -

Parent Activities

1. Allow your child to assist in measuring baking ingredients to build number sense with fractions. Ask questions such as the following:

- How many $\frac{1}{2}$ cups of flour are equal to 1 whole cup?
- Is $\frac{2}{3}$ cup of sugar more than $\frac{1}{2}$ cup or less than $\frac{1}{2}$ cup?
- Is $\frac{2}{3}$ cup of sugar closer to $\frac{1}{2}$ or closer to 1?

2. Use a ruler to show your child how to estimate when finding sums or differences of fractional numbers. For example, a length of $1\frac{7}{8}$ is close to 2 inches. A measure of $\frac{5}{8}$ inch is close to $\frac{1}{2}$ inch. The estimated sum is $2 + \frac{1}{2}$ or $2\frac{1}{2}$. Discuss inch measures on the ruler that can be rounded to $\frac{1}{4}$, $\frac{1}{2}$, $\frac{3}{4}$, and 1.

1 Matt competes in the 100-meter dash. After running $\frac{40}{100}$ of the race, Matt trips and falls. Place an X on the number line below to show where Matt tripped.

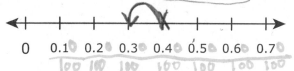

0   0.1   0.2   0.3   0.4   0.5   0.6   0.7
   100 100 100 100 100 100 100

What decimal number represents the part of the race Matt ran before he tripped?

Answer: _0.30 = 0.3_

2 Arjun needs to locate the fraction $\frac{29}{100}$ on this decimal number line. Locate and label a point to show where Arjun should place this fraction.

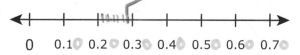

0   0.1   0.2   0.3   0.4   0.5   0.6   0.7

Why did you place the point where you did?

Answer: _Because_
#29 comes right
befor #30

3 Reese follows a pattern in her exercise program. She runs $\frac{2}{10}$ mile and then walks $\frac{1}{10}$ mile. She completes this pattern a total of 3 times. Use the number line below to show Reese's exercise pattern.

0   0.2   0.4   0.6   0.8   1   1.2   1.4

At what distance from the starting point does Reese complete her pattern? Write the answer as a fraction and as a decimal number.

Fraction: _9/10_

Decimal: _0.9_

Use the number line to answer questions 4–6.

Mrs. Lee wears a pedometer to track the distance, in miles, she walks each day while at work. Before leaving the office, Mrs. Lee records the distances on this number line and labels the day of the week.

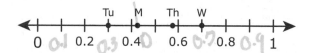

0   0.1   0.2   0.3   0.4   0.6   0.7   0.8   0.9   1

4 On which day of the week did Mrs. Lee walk a distance of $\frac{7}{10}$ mile?

Answer: _wednesday_

On which day of the week did Mrs. Lee walk a distance of $\frac{43}{100}$ mile?

Answer: _monday_

As a fraction, about how far did Mrs. Lee walk on Thursday?

Answer: _$\frac{0.60}{100}$_

5 On Friday, Mrs. Lee left the office without recording the distance she walked. Her pedometer read 0.88. Locate this distance on Mrs. Lee's number line. What fraction corresponds to this distance?

Answer: _$\frac{.88}{100}$_

6 Could Mrs. Lee use this number line to record the total distance she walked for the week?

Answer: _Yes_

Explain your answer.

she could add
up the total
distances!

1 Bradley participated in a Putt-Putt® golf tournament. The number line shows the fraction of the distance from the tee to the hole his first putt traveled.

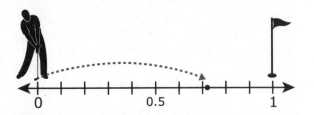

Which best represents the fraction of the distance that Bradley's first putt traveled?

Ⓐ $\frac{7}{10}$

Ⓒ $\frac{73}{10}$

Ⓑ $\frac{73}{100}$

Ⓓ $\frac{7}{100}$

2 Jeremy plays a math game with 3 friends. Each time Jeremy rolls the dice, he answers a question and moves a token along the number line. After 5 turns, Jeremy's token is located a distance of 0.63 from START.

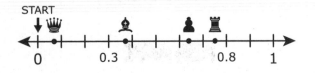

Which of the following is Jeremy's token?

Ⓕ ♛

Ⓖ ♗

Ⓗ ♟

Ⓙ ♜

3 Gretchen notices that her centimeter ruler is similar to a number line marked in tenths. She places her pencil above the centimeter ruler.

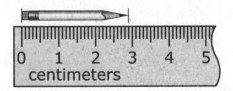

Which fraction and decimal best show the distance from 0 on Gretchen's ruler that corresponds to the length, in centimeters, of the pencil?

Ⓐ $2\frac{9}{10}$ and 2.9

Ⓑ $2\frac{90}{100}$ and 2.90

Ⓒ $\frac{29}{10}$ and 2.9

Ⓓ All of the above

4 On the number lines below, the distance between 0 and 1 represents 1 mile. On which number line does point Z represent a distance of 0.35 mile from zero?

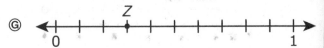

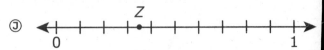

motivation**math**™LEVEL 4

1 The quarterback of the football team threw a long pass from the goal line. The pass traveled $\frac{62}{100}$ the length of the football field. Which number line shows a point that represents this distance from the goal line?

(A)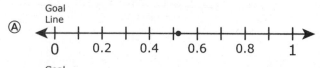

(B)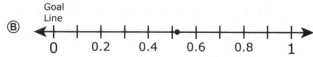

(C)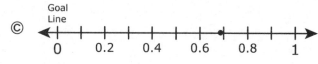

(D)

2 Lionel rides the Polar Express™ Train from point *A* to point *B*. The train makes a stop along the way to serve hot chocolate to the passengers.

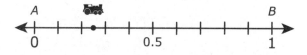

At what fraction of the distance from the start of the trip does the train stop?

(F) 25/10

(G) $\frac{2}{100}$

(H) $\frac{25}{100}$

(J) $2\frac{5}{10}$

3 The distance from home plate, labeled 0, to the outfield fence, labeled 1, is shown by this number line.

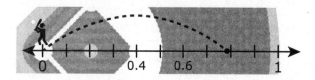

When Roberta bats, she hits a fly ball to center field. Which decimal number best represents the fraction of the distance from home plate to the outfield fence that Roberta's ball travels?

(A) 0.9

(B) 0.88

(C) 0.78

(D) 0.72

4 Devin conducts a science investigation to find the distance, in inches, covered by a snail in one minute. He creates this number line to display the results.

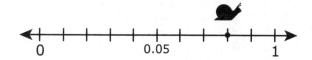

According to Devin's number line, what distance from the starting point, labeled 0, did the snail travel in one minute?

(F) $\frac{8}{10}$ in.

(G) $\frac{80}{100}$ in.

(H) $\frac{8}{100}$ in.

(J) $\frac{80}{10}$ in.

Use the number line to answer questions 1–3.

Jessi and her dad played tennis on Saturday morning. The number line represents the tennis court, with the net located at 0.5. The distance the ball traveled on each of Jessi's first 4 serves is marked on the number line and labeled with the serve number.

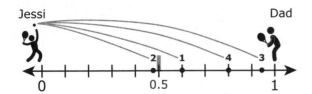

1 Which best represents the part of the distance between Jessi and Dad that her first serve traveled?

Ⓐ 0.94   Ⓒ 0.90

Ⓑ 0.60   Ⓓ 0.47

2 Which serve traveled $\frac{94}{100}$ of the distance between Jessi and her dad?

Ⓕ Serve 1

Ⓖ Serve 2

Ⓗ Serve 3

Ⓙ Serve 4

3 Jessi's fifth serve landed a distance between Serves 1 and 2. Which of these fractions could represent the distance Jessi's fifth serve traveled?

Ⓐ $\frac{54}{100}$ Ⓒ $\frac{54}{10}$

Ⓑ $\frac{4}{10}$ Ⓓ $\frac{62}{100}$

4 Adrianna drew a number line to show the distance, in kilometers, between her house and her friend Margo's house. Adrianna's number line is shown below.

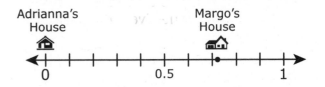

Which fraction and decimal correctly represent the distance, in miles, from Adrianna's house to Margo's house?

Ⓕ $\frac{73}{10}$ and 7.3

Ⓖ $7\frac{3}{100}$ and 7.03

Ⓗ $\frac{73}{100}$ and 7.3

Ⓙ Not here

5 Miguel observed a centimeter ruler. He said, "Each centimeter is divided into tenths. This looks like a number line!" Miguel used the centimeter ruler to report the distance an ant crawled along his desktop.

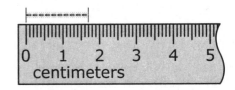

Which shows the decimal number that represents this distance?

Ⓐ 0.7 cm

Ⓑ 1.07 cm

Ⓒ 1.7 cm

Ⓓ 0.17 cm

1 Mary Alice visits her grandparents' farm in the country. She enjoys walking the path to the river. Mary Alice draws a number line that shows the distances, in miles, from the farm to favorite spots along the path to the river. Mary Alice's number line is shown below.

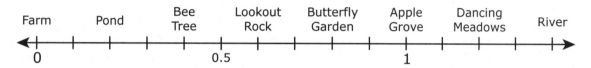

One day, Mary Alice walks 0.3 mile from the farm and stops to observe a turtle walking across the path. From that point, she walks less than 1 mile but more than 0.7 mile and stops to have a picnic at one of her favorite spots. Where does Mary Alice eat lunch?

Answer: _____

What decimal number shows the distance from the farm to this location?

Answer: _____

2 Vince invited 3 friends to his party. The boys competed in a beanbag toss game. Each friend tossed a different beanbag as shown below.

Vince   Reginald   Marcus   Leo

Use the clues to determine the distance, in meters, of each boy's toss from the starting point, labeled 0, to the target, labeled 1. Use the number line to locate a point that represents the distance of each toss, and mark the distance with the symbol found on the guest's beanbag.

- Vince's toss has a digit 2 that is equal to $\frac{2}{100}$. The digit in the tenths place is twice this digit.

- Reginald's toss fell short of the hole in the target by $\frac{3}{100}$ meter.

- Marcus tossed his beanbag exactly twice as far as Vince's toss.

- Reginald's toss is equal to the sum of Vince's toss and Leo's toss.

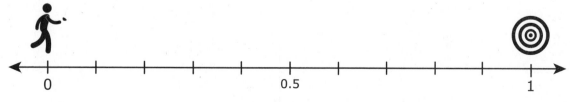

Unit 14 Journal/Vocabulary Activity

Journal

Throughout this unit, distances in various sporting events have been represented as distances on number lines. Using the number line below, create an original sports problem in which fractions or decimals to the tenths or hundredth place could be represented as distances from 0.

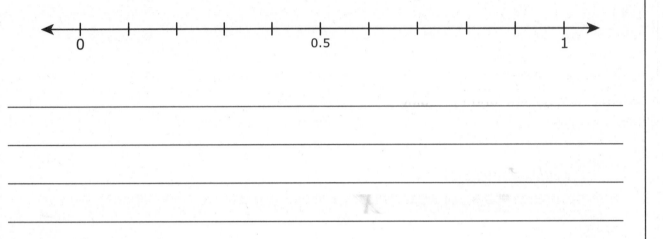

_____

_____

_____

_____

Vocabulary Activity

Use words and pictures to explain how $\frac{2}{10}$ and 0.2 are the same distance from 0 on a number line as $\frac{20}{100}$ and 0.20.

_____

_____

_____

_____

   motivation**math**™ LEVEL 4

Motivation Molly says, "You're very talented!"

Roll and Race

Play *Roll and Race* with a partner. Each player needs a pencil and a game board. Each pair of players needs 2 number cubes or dice. The object of the game is to ride the number line the greatest distance in 10 turns. In turn, each player rolls the number cubes/dice and adds the numbers rolled. The sum tells the number of hundredths the player's car moves. For example, rolling 2 and 5 means the player moves a distance of $\frac{7}{100}$ from the starting point, 0. For each turn, players record the numbers rolled, the sum, and the distance traveled. The player identifies the point by marking an "X" on his/her number line and recording the total distance on the chart. The winner is the first player to cross the finish line, labeled 1, on his/her game board.

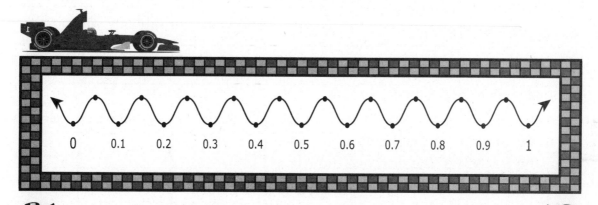

Turn Number	Numbers Rolled	Sum of Numbers Rolled	Length of Move	Total Distance Traveled
1				
2				
3				
4				
5				
6				
7				
8				
9				
10				

1 The length of Olivia's bedroom is represented by this number line. The door to her room corresponds with 0, and the opposite wall corresponds with 1.

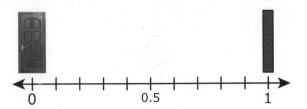

In the distance from the door to the opposite wall, Olivia places her bed at $\frac{35}{100}$ and a desk at $\frac{7}{10}$. Mark and label two points on the number line to represent the bed, *B*, and the desk, *D*.

2 The Hall family drove from Tyler to Waco. Mr. Hall said, "We're between $\frac{8}{10}$ and $\frac{9}{10}$ of the way there." Complete the number line below. Locate a point that could represent the fraction of the distance the family traveled.

Tyler   Waco

0   1

What decimal represents the distance from zero the family has traveled?

✂ **Answer:** _____

3 Charlie is the place kicker on his football team. Each day Charlie makes several practice kicks. The distance between 0 and 1 on this number line represents the length of a football field. Four of Charlie's kicks are shown as points on the number line, labeled 1 through 4.

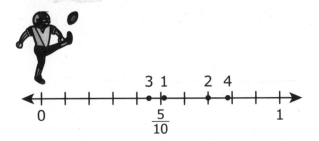

Complete the table by writing a fraction and the equivalent decimal number to represent Charlie's kicks from the goal line, 0.

Kick	Fraction	Decimal
1		
2		
3		
4		

Parent Activities

1. Use a tape measure marked in centimeters, and discuss that a tape measure represents a number line. Each centimeter is divided into 10 parts, or tenths. Allow your child to explore the different "points" on the tape by measuring the lengths of objects and reporting the distances from 0, using whole numbers and fractions (e.g., "I measure the length of my shoe and see that it is $22\frac{4}{10}$ centimeters or 22.4 centimeters.").

2. Use sidewalk chalk to draw a number line, and divide it into 10 equal sections. Label the first mark with 0 and the last mark with 1. Have your child use a different color chalk to label the decimals for each remaining mark. Discuss the hundredths that come between the labeled tenths (e.g., The decimal numbers 0.51, 0.52,... come between 0.5 and 0.6.). Call various decimals and have your child stand at the decimal locations.

1 Scott created a video presentation to show his work on a science project. The first segment of the presentation was 2.1 minutes long, and the second segment was 0.97 minutes long.

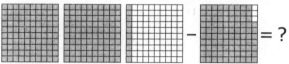

First Segment   Second Segment

Write and solve an equation to find how much longer the first segment of Scott's presentation was than the second segment.

Answer: ___1.03___

2 Grace selects two numbers from the box and adds to find a sum of 73.96.

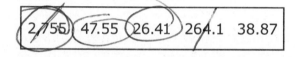

2,755   47.55   26.41   264.1   38.87

What two numbers did Grace select?

Answers: __2,490.9__ and _____

Adalynn also selects two numbers from the box. She finds a difference of 2,490.9. What two numbers did Adalynn select?

Answers: _____ and _____

3 Stephen made a banner for the school play. He used 1.5 meters of red fabric and 1.25 meters of blue fabric. Use the number line to show the total length of fabric Stephen used for the banner.

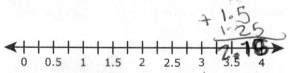

0   0.5   1   1.5   2   2.5   3   3.5   4

How much fabric did Stephen use?

Answer: ___2.75___

4 On Friday, 3,516 people attended a play at Oakbrook Theater. On Saturday, 2,095 people attended the play, and 2,846 people attended on Sunday. Write and solve an equation to find the total number of people who attended the play on the three days.

5 Anna broke a stick of gum into two pieces. One piece was 2.8 centimeters long. The other piece was 2.5 centimeters long.

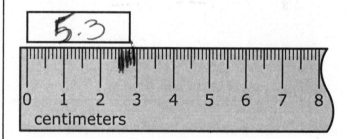

0   1   2   3   4   5   6   7   8
centimeters

How many centimeters long was the whole stick of gum?

Answer: ___5.3___

6 At birth, Mrs. Aaron's triplets weighed 5.75 pounds, 5.9 pounds, and 6.05 pounds. What was the total weight of Mrs. Aaron's triplets?

Answer: ___17.7___

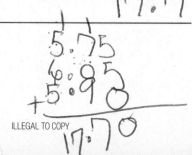

Use the chart to answer questions 1 and 2.

The Alba Food Bank conducted a canned food drive. The chart shows the number of cans collected each day for 6 days.

Food Drive Collection

Day	Number of Cans
Monday	1,138
Tuesday	1,039
Wednesday	1,518
Thursday	2,220
Friday	2,958
Saturday	3,018

1 How many total cans of food were collected on Thursday, Friday, and Saturday?

Ⓐ 8,296

Ⓒ 7,186

Ⓑ 8,196

Ⓓ 8,096

2 How many more cans of food were collected on Friday and Saturday than on Monday and Tuesday?

Ⓕ 3,799

Ⓗ 3,899

Ⓖ 3,809

Ⓙ 8,153

3 Misty buys 9.5 pounds of peaches at a fruit stand. She uses 2.8 pounds in a cobbler and 3.4 pounds to make peach jam. She gives the remaining peaches to her neighbor. How many pounds of peaches does Misty give her neighbor?

Ⓐ 15.7 lb

Ⓒ 3.3 lb

Ⓑ 10.1 lb

Ⓓ 6.1 lb

4 Four students in Mrs. Johnson's class modeled decimal numbers with base 10 blocks to solve this equation.

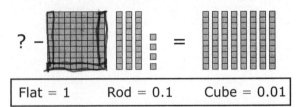

| Flat = 1 | Rod = 0.1 | Cube = 0.01 |

Abby's answer was 0.54, Brian's answer was 1.14, Carter's answer was 1.41, and Dennis thought the answer was 2.14. Which student solved the problem correctly?

Ⓧ Abby

Ⓧ Carter

Ⓧ Brian

● Dennis

5 Mr. Martin gave his students hundredths squares and asked them to shade the first letters of their names. Javier, Michelle, and Hannah created the squares shown.

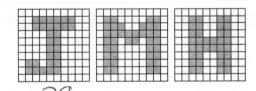

Which statement about the students' hundredths square initials is **NOT** correct?

Ⓐ Michelle's initial is 0.04 smaller than Hannah's initial.

Ⓑ Hannah's initial is 0.07 larger than Javier's initial.

Ⓒ Javier's initial is 0.11 smaller than Michelle's initial.

Ⓓ Together, Javier and Hannah shaded 0.65 small squares.

motivation**math**™LEVEL 4

Application

i

Apply

1   The table shows the average numbers of $100, $10, and $1 bills printed each day in 2012 by the United States Bureau of Printing and Engraving.

Type of Bill	Average Number Printed Each Day	Total Daily Value ($)
$100	8,280,000	
$ 10	1,788,493	
$ 1	5,540,822	

Complete the table to show the total daily value for each type of bill. What is the total daily value of the bills printed? Show your work.

Answer: _____

Analysis

i

Analyze

2   Based on the place value patterns formed when multiplying a number by 10 or 100, how will multiplying a number by 1,000 or 10,000 affect the product? Use words and numbers to explain your answer.

_____

_____

_____

_____

Unit 16 Journal/Vocabulary Activity

Journal

Application

i

Apply

Describe a real-world situation that requires you to multiply a number by 10 or 100.

_____

_____

_____

_____

_____

Vocabulary Activity

Write 4,578 × 10 using expanded notation.

_____

Circle the digit in the number 7,976,470 that will have a value of 7,000 when this number is multiplied by 100.

Explain why, when 10 is a factor, each digit moves one place to the left, and when 100 is a factor, each digit moves two places to the left.

_____

_____

 motivation**math**™LEVEL 4 ©2014 mentoring**minds**.com

Motivation Molly says, "Marvelous math master!"

Multiply to the Moon

Play *Multiply to the Moon* with a partner. Players need two number cubes/dice, two different colors of crayons (one color for each player), and one game board to share. In turn, each player rolls the dice and multiplies the numbers rolled. The player then multiplies the product by 10 and colors the number of hundred squares equal to the total. For example, if a player rolls 4 and 3, the product of 12 is multiplied by 10 and the player colors 120, or 1 full square and 20 sections of another square. If there are not enough blank squares, the player passes. When all possible squares are colored, the winner is the player with the most squares colored.

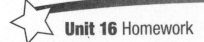

Unit 16 Homework

1 Use expanded notation to show each place value for this problem.

$$945 \times 10$$

_____

_____

2 Complete the following table to show patterns when multiplying by 10 or 100.

Number	× 10	× 100
43	430	
630		
		345,600
580		58,000
	6,470,000	

Use place value to explain the patterns found in your answers.

_____

_____

_____

3 There are 45,692 students in the Vera Cruz School District. Every student in the district donated 10 cans of food. How many total cans of food did the students donate?

Answer: _____

4 Complete Mark's math equations.

$64 \times$ _____ $= 640$

$640 \times$ _____ $= 6,400$

$6,400 \times$ _____ $= 64,000$

$64,000 \times$ _____ $= 640,000$

Write the next 2 equations in Mark's pattern.

_____

_____

What is the missing factor in each equation?

Answer: _____

✂ -

Parent Activities

1. Have your child toss two number cubes or dice and find the sum of the digits. Multiply the sum by 10 or 100. Ask your child to explain how the values of the digits change when multiplied by 10 or 100.

2. Use a trip to the grocery store as an opportunity to reinforce multiplying by 10. Call attention to the price of an item, and help your child determine what the total cost would be if purchasing 10 of the item (e.g., One carton of ice cream costs $3. How could we quickly find the total cost of 10 cartons?). Help your child understand that the digits move one place value to the left when multiplied by 10.

 motivation**math**™LEVEL 4

1 Kim, Leo, and Mack each collect small rocks for an art project. Kim has 10 bags of 10 rocks. Leo has 13 bags of 10 rocks. Kim and Leo each use base 10 blocks to find how many rocks they have, as shown in these area models.

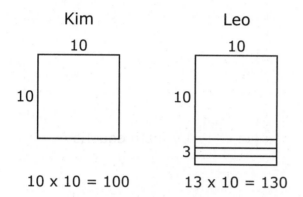

10 x 10 = 100   13 x 10 = 130

Mack uses the area model below to find his total number of rocks. Record a number on each line to match Mack's model.

Mack

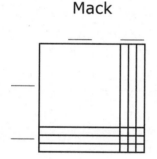

Write and solve an equation to find the total number of rocks in Mack's collection.

Equation: _____

Kim does not understand how Mack's equation matches the model. How could he explain it to her?

_____

_____

_____

2 A perfect square is a number that is the product of 2 equal factors. In problem 1, Kim's model shows that 100 is a perfect square because $10 \times 10 = 100$. Which other student has a model that represents a perfect square?

Answer: _____

Explain your answer.

_____

_____

3 A first-grade teacher stacks boxes of pencils in an array on the shelf. Each box contains 17 pencils.

Write and solve an equation to find the total number of pencils in the boxes.

Equation: _____

4 Larry collects 16 buckets of golf balls at the golf course. Each bucket holds 25 golf balls. Larry uses this area model to calculate the total number of golf balls he collects.

	10	10	5
10	100	100	50
6	60	60	30

Write and solve the multiplication equation Larry's model represents.

Equation: _____

1 Jane's bedroom is 15 feet long and 12 feet wide. She draws this area model to represent the floor of the room.

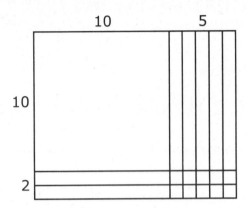

Which equation represents the product shown in Jane's model?

Ⓐ 105 × 102 = 207

Ⓑ 12 × 15 = 180

Ⓒ 12 × 12 = 144

Ⓓ 15 × 12 = 110

2 Casey reads 21 pages every night. Which model shows a way Casey could use base 10 blocks to find the total number of pages she reads in 24 nights?

Ⓕ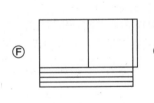

Ⓗ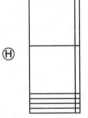

Ⓖ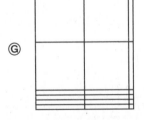

Ⓙ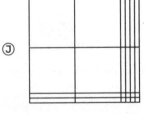

3 An elephant's heart beats about 25 times in 1 minute. The area model below can be used to find the total number of times an elephant's heart beats in 45 minutes.

	40	5
20	40 x 20 = 800	5 x 20 = 100
5	40 x 5 = 200	5 x 5 = 25

What is the product of 45 × 25?

Ⓐ 1,125

Ⓑ 925

Ⓒ 1,250

Ⓓ 945

4 The windows on the front of an office building form an array that is a perfect square. This model represents the top row of windows.

Which method could be used to find the total number of windows on the front of the office building?

Ⓕ Find the product of 1 and 14: 1 × 14 = 14

Ⓖ Double 14: 2 × 14 = 28

Ⓗ Find the product of 14 and 14: 14 × 14 = 196

Ⓙ Find the sum of 14 and 14: 14 + 14 = 28

1 Travis buys treat bags for his birthday party. Each bag contains exactly 48 treats. Travis arranges the bags as shown.

Which equation can be used to find the total number of treats in the bags Travis buys?

Ⓐ 14 × 48 = 672

Ⓑ 48 × 48 = 2,304

Ⓒ 7 × 48 = 336

Ⓓ 2 × 48 = 96

2 Gregory helps the school principal by counting 16 school newsletters for each of the 22 classrooms. He uses this area model to find the total number of newsletters.

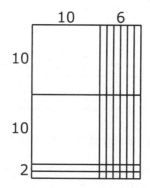

What is the product Gregory finds?

Ⓕ 262   Ⓗ 220

Ⓖ 296   Ⓙ 352

3 A construction company buys 54 boxes of nails. Each box contains 76 nails. This area model can be used to find the total number of nails.

	70	6
50	50 x 70 = 3,500	50 x 6 = 300
4	4 x 70 = 280	4 x 6 = 24

Based on the model, what is the next step in finding the total number of nails?

Ⓐ Add 54 and 76 to find a sum of 130.

Ⓑ Add (70 × 50) + (6 × 4) to find a sum of 3,524.

Ⓒ Add 3,500 + 300 + 280 + 24 to find a sum of 4,104.

Ⓓ Multiply 3,500 × 300 × 280 × 24 to find a product of 4,804.

4 Fancy Cake Bakery orders 17 boxes of cake trays. There are 20 trays in each box. Which shows a model that represents the total number of cake trays?

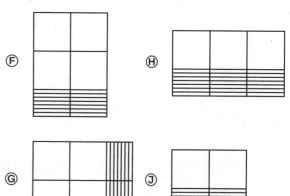

Unit 17 Assessment

1 A school principal buys 12 dozen donuts for the Donuts with Dad breakfast. Which area model best represents the total number of donuts the principal buys?

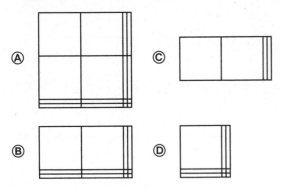

3 Ben bakes 60 cookies. This array shows the number of chocolate chips in each cookie.

Which equation can be used to find the total number of chocolate chips Ben uses?

Ⓐ $1 \times 13 = 13$

Ⓑ $13 \times 60 = 880$

Ⓒ $13 \times 13 = 169$

Ⓓ $60 \times 13 = 780$

4 Abner receives a toy catalog in the mail. The catalog has 25 pages and shows 11 toys on each page. Abner uses this model to find the total number of toys in the catalog.

2 Each of the 34 members of the travel club plans to read a travel guide book this month. The book has 86 pages. This model can be used to find the total number of pages the travel club members will read this month.

	80	6
30	30 x 80 = 2,400	30 x 6 = 180
4	4 x 80 = 320	4 x 6 = 24

What product does the model represent?

Ⓕ 2,924

Ⓖ 2,720

Ⓗ 3,140

Ⓙ 2,980

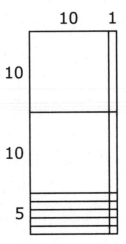

What total does Abner's model represent?

Ⓕ 36, because he adds 30 + 6 to find the total.

Ⓖ 275, because he adds 200 + 70 + 5 to find the total.

Ⓗ 375, because he multiplies 25 × 11 to find the total.

Ⓙ 265, because he adds 100 + 100 + 50 + 15 to find the total.

 motivation**math**™LEVEL 4 ©2014 mentoring**minds**.com

1 Study the pattern below. Draw the next two figures in the pattern and label each figure with a number.

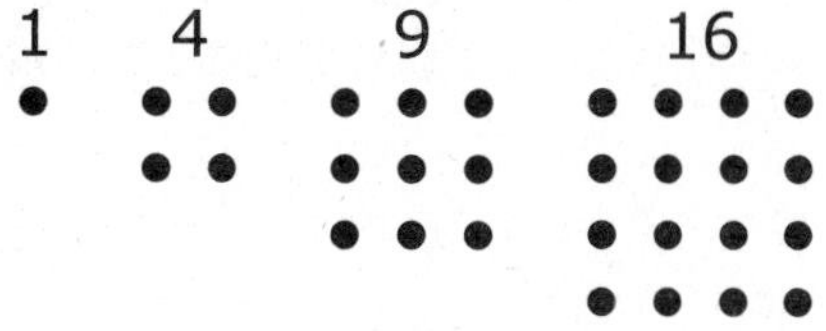

Why do you think the figures in this pattern are called square numbers?

____

____

What number would be the label for the 15th term in this pattern?

Answer: ____________

2 This area model represents the product of two 2-digit numbers. Record a number in each blank to complete the model.

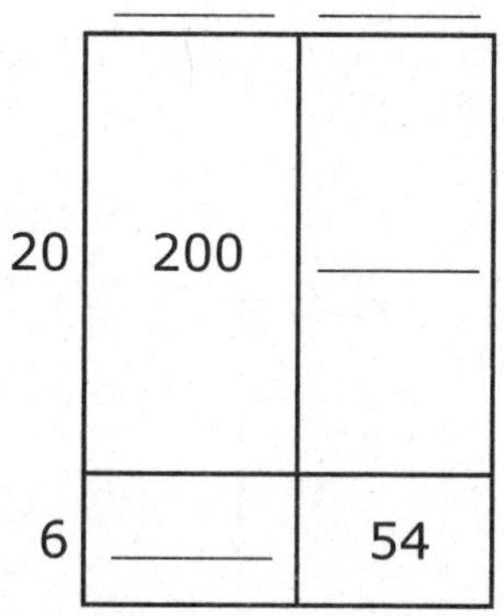

What equation does the model represent?

Equation: ____

Unit 17 Journal/Vocabulary Activity

Journal

Why is the answer to 12 × 12 the same as the answer to 6 × 24? Use words, numbers, and pictures to explain your thinking.

_____

_____

_____

_____

_____

Vocabulary Activity

Use the term *area model*, *array*, or *equation* to label each representation. Then, circle the representation of a product that is a perfect square.

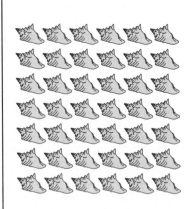

$$40 \times 44 = 1{,}760$$

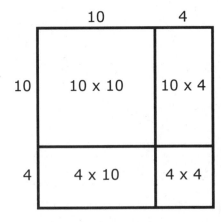

	10	4
10	10 x 10	10 x 4
4	4 x 10	4 x 4

_____   _____   _____

    motivation**math**™LEVEL 4

Motivation Mike says, "I can't get over how smart you are!"

Battle of the Books

Play *Battle of the Books* with a friend. The object of the game is to be the first player to build an area model that can be used to correctly solve a multiplication problem. Each player needs a game board, a set of base 10 blocks, and a die. Each pair of players needs a pencil and paper clip for the spinner. Together, players read the problem below. As the problem is read, each player rolls a die 4 times and records the rolled digits in the appropriate spaces in the problem. When each player has created a unique word problem, player 1 spins the spinner and takes the corresponding block to begin building an area model for his/her problem. Players alternate turns. If a player does not wish to use the spun block for the area model, play passes with no block taken. When a player has completed his/her area model using base 10 blocks, the player sketches the model and records the product on the game sheet. If the product is correct, the player is the winner.

There are _____ _____ bookshelves in a bookstore.
             roll 1 roll 2

Each shelf holds _____ _____ books.
                 roll 3 roll 4

To determine the total number of books, the store manager writes the following equation.

$$\underset{\textbf{roll 1}\quad\textbf{roll 2}}{\underline{\quad\quad}\ \underline{\quad\quad}} \times \underset{\textbf{roll 3}\quad\textbf{roll 4}}{\underline{\quad\quad}\ \underline{\quad\quad}} = ?$$

What is the total number of books in the bookstore?

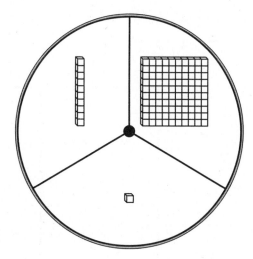

My Model

Answer: _____ books

1 Each of Mrs. Howard's 27 students writes 52 math facts for homework. How many total math facts do Mrs. Howard's students write? Complete this area model to find the solution.

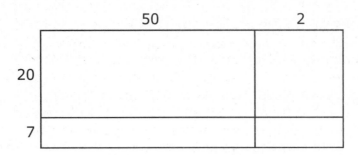

What multiplication equation does the area model represent?

Equation: _____

Explain how you used the area model to find the product.

_____

_____

2 Mrs. Ali arranges gifts for her students in this pattern. Each gift contains 36 tiny erasers.

Write and solve a multiplication equation to find the total number of tiny erasers Mrs. Ali gives her students.

36 36 36 36 36
36 36 36 36 36
36 36 36 36 36

Equation: _____

✂ --

Parent Activities

1. Have your child count the number of rows in a rectangular parking lot and the number of parking spaces per row. Multiply the two numbers together to find the number of cars the parking lot can hold.

2. Count the number of rows of ceiling or floor tiles in a room and the number of tiles per row. Multiply the numbers to determine how many tiles are in the room.

3. Challenge your child to use objects such as pennies or paper clips to create a rectangular array. Have your child write and solve an equation to represent the array. Repeat the process with a different number of objects.

 motivation**math**™LEVEL 4

1 Eve had 112 apples. She made fruit baskets by placing 7 apples in each basket as shown below.

What division equation shows how many baskets were used?

Answer: _____

2 Marta drew this area model to find the quotient of 108 ÷ 9.

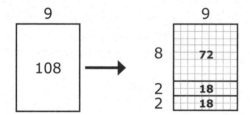

What quotient did Marta find?

Answer: _____

Explain how Marta used the area model to find the quotient.

_____

_____

_____

3 Flint used base 10 blocks to find the quotient of 238 ÷ 2.

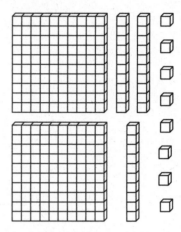

What is the quotient?

Answer: _____

Explain the steps Flint used to find this quotient.

_____

_____

_____

4 Star Stadium has been sold out for the last 4 weekends. On Friday, 3,424 fans attended the baseball game between the Tennessee Tornadoes and the Mississippi Mudcats. The stadium is divided into eight equal sections. How many fans were seated in each section?

Draw a model to help you solve this problem.

Write and solve an equation that represents this problem.

Answer: _____

Unit 19 Guided Practice

1 Jarrett drew the model below to solve a division problem.

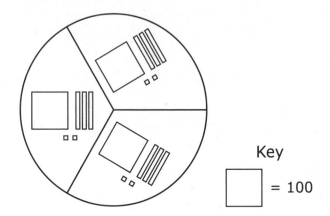

Key

□ = 100

Which equation matches Jarrett's model?

Ⓐ 132 ÷ 3 = 44

Ⓑ 132 ÷ 2 = 66

Ⓒ 18 ÷ 3 = 6

Ⓓ 396 ÷ 3 = 132

2 Julie drew the following model to help solve 1,456 ÷ 7.

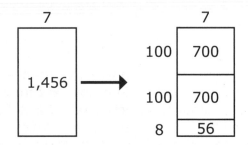

What is the next step Julie must use to find the final quotient?

Ⓕ Divide 100 by 7.

Ⓖ Subtract 208 from 1,456.

Ⓗ Find the sum of 100, 100, and 8.

Ⓙ Multiply 8 and 200.

3 Rafael drew the model below.

Which problem is **NOT** represented by Rafael's model?

Ⓐ Rafael has 112 marbles. He divides the marbles into bags by placing 14 marbles in each bag. How many bags does Rafael fill?

Ⓑ Rafael has 8 bags of marbles. Each bag contains 14 marbles. How many total marbles does Rafael have?

Ⓒ Rafael has 112 marbles. He gives 8 friends a dozen marbles each. How many marbles does Rafael have now?

Ⓓ Rafael has 112 marbles. He divides them equally into 8 bags. How many marbles are in each bag?

4 Every morning, Gail stocks the checkout counters at the grocery store with shopping bags. The store receives 1,260 bags each day. If the bags are equally distributed among 9 checkout counters, which equation shows how many bags each counter receives?

Ⓕ 1,260 ÷ 9 = 14

Ⓖ 1,260 ÷ 9 = 104

Ⓗ 1,260 ÷ 9 = 130

Ⓙ 1,260 ÷ 9 = 140

©2014 mentoring**minds**.com

1 Charlene used base 10 blocks to model a division problem.

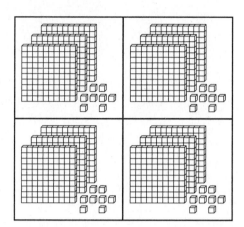

Which equation is shown by Charlene's model?

Ⓐ 308 ÷ 4 = 77

Ⓑ 1,208 ÷ 4 = 302

Ⓒ 1,232 ÷ 4 = 308

Ⓓ 1,232 ÷ 4 = 38

2 Mr. Crump purchased five TVs to donate to the children's wing at the hospital. The total cost of the TVs was $2,550. To show the cost of each TV, Mr. Crump begins to draw an area model.

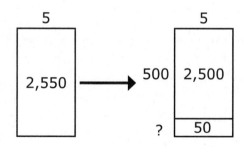

What number should replace the question mark in Mr. Crump's model?

Ⓕ 5   Ⓗ 50

Ⓖ 10   Ⓙ 100

3 Which model does **NOT** represent 120 ÷ 3?

Ⓐ
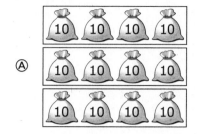

Ⓑ

Ⓒ

Ⓓ

4 Mrs. Monk prepared 672 fluid ounces of punch for a party. She poured the punch into 3 different punch bowls. Each serving of punch was 8 fluid ounces. Which equation shows how many servings of punch Mrs. Monk prepared?

Ⓕ 672 ÷ 3 = 224

Ⓖ 672 ÷ 8 = 84

Ⓗ 672 ÷ 5 = 134

Ⓙ 672 ÷ 8 = 804

1 Andy formed the following model of base 10 blocks to help him find the quotient of 256 ÷ 2.

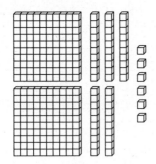

Which is the correct quotient?

Ⓐ 100   Ⓒ 128

Ⓑ 123   Ⓓ 256

2 Students at Travis School collected a total of 1,344 cans of food. Each of 8 classes collected the same amount. Jeremy drew the area model below to show how many cans his class collected.

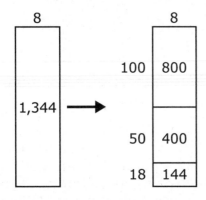

What is the final step needed to determine the number of cans Jeremy's class collected?

Ⓕ Divide 18 by 8 to find a quotient of 2 with a remainder of 2.

Ⓖ Find the sum of the partial quotients 100 + 50 + 18.

Ⓗ Find the sum of 800 + 400 + 144.

Ⓙ Subtract the sum of 100 + 50 + 18 from 1,344.

3 Dawn drew the following model.

Which problem **CANNOT** be represented by Dawn's model?

Ⓐ Dawn helps stock the stations for a baking contest. She has 120 eggs. She places 6 eggs at each baking station. How many baking stations does Dawn stock?

Ⓑ Dawn has 20 baskets. She places 6 eggs in each basket. How many total eggs does Dawn have?

Ⓒ Dawn has 10 dozen eggs. She places the eggs into baskets that each hold 6 eggs. How many baskets does Dawn use?

Ⓓ Dawn has 120 eggs. She places a dozen eggs into each basket. How many baskets does Dawn use?

4 Kaden ate 3 meals each day for a total of 1,926 calories. He followed this pattern for 6 days. Kaden ate the same number of calories at each meal. Which equation shows how many calories were in Kaden's breakfast meal?

Ⓕ 1,926 ÷ 3 = 642

Ⓖ 1,926 ÷ 6 = 321

Ⓗ 1,926 ÷ 9 = 214

Ⓙ 1,926 ÷ 3 = 942

1 Joseph chose a mystery number. His mystery number is greater than 10 and less than 60. The mystery number has a remainder of 1 when divided by 6 and a remainder of 2 when divided by 5. What number could be Joseph's mystery number?

Answer: _____

Explain how you found your answer.

_____

_____

_____

2 Three students created area models to represent the quotient of $3,438 \div 9$. The models are shown below.

	Tia		Levi		Wes
	9		9		9

Tia:
200 | 1,800
150 | 1,350
30 | 270
2 | 18

Levi:
100 | 900
100 | 900
100 | 900
50 | 450
30 | 270
2 | 18

Wes:
300 | 2,700
80 | 720
2 | 18

Who drew a correct model? Justify your answer.

_____

_____

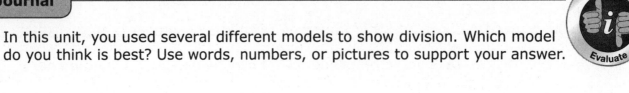

Journal

In this unit, you used several different models to show division. Which model do you think is best? Use words, numbers, or pictures to support your answer.

_____

_____

_____

_____

Vocabulary Activity

The word box lists words and phrases that might be used when solving a division problem.

Word Box			
area model	divide	dividing	equation
array	dividend	divisor	quotient
digit	divides	equal groups	remainder

Use at least four words from the word box to create a tongue twister about division.

_____

_____

_____

_____

motivation**math**™LEVEL 4   ©2014 mentoring**minds**.com

Motivation Mike says, "You should be proud of yourself!"

A-maze-ing Division

Play *A-maze-ing Division* with a partner. Each pair of players needs two game markers and a 1–6 number cube. Players start on opposite ends of the game board. In turn, each player rolls the number cube and moves to any circle that is evenly divisible by the number on the cube. For all remaining moves, the player rolls the number cube and moves to a connecting number only if it is divisible by the number on the cube. If there is no connecting number that is evenly divisible by the number on the cube, the player loses a turn. The winner is the first player to reach the opposite end of the game board.

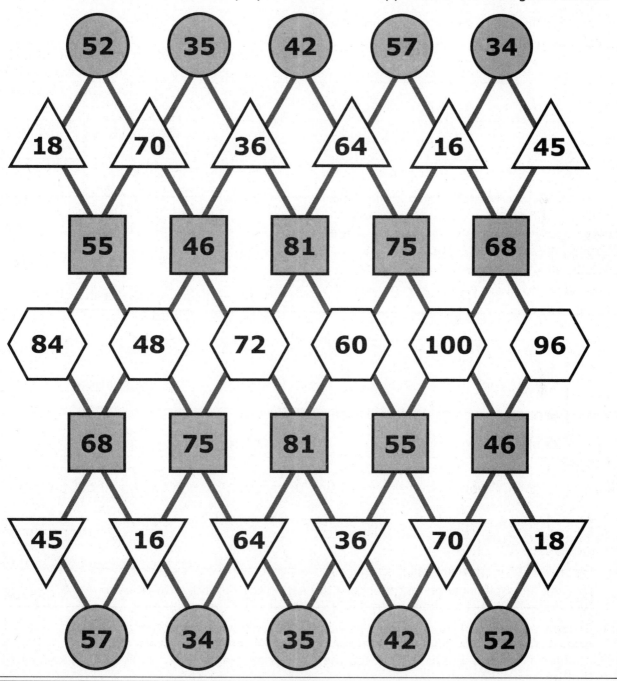

Unit 19 Homework

1 Jace drew an area model to find the quotient of 216 ÷ 6.

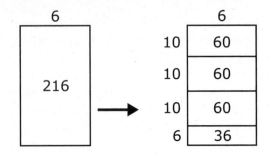

Show the final step and the quotient for Jace's computation.

2 Zoey collected 426 small seashells. She used all the shells to decorate 3 boxes, placing an equal number of shells on each box. Draw a model to show how many seashells Zoey placed on each box.

What equation can be used to represent your model?

Answer: _____

3 There were 4,128 young singers who auditioned for the singing competition. The producers separated the singers into 8 equal groups. Write an equation showing how many singers were in each group.

Answer: _____

4 Steffy wants to show her friend how to compute 435 ÷ 3 with base 10 blocks. She starts by building the model below.

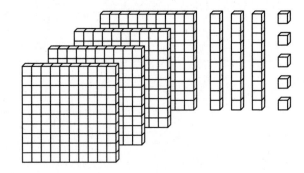

Record in words the steps Steffy should show her friend.

_____

_____

_____

_____

✂ -

Parent Activities

1. Use flash cards to review division facts and build fluency with your child. Discuss the multiplication fact that is in the same fact family as the division fact (e.g., 72 ÷ 8 = 9 is related to 8 × 9 = 72.).

2. Discuss situations in the real world in which a quantity is split into equal groups. Help your child find items around the house that demonstrate division (e.g., The total number of cookies in a box is 36, and the cookies are arranged in 3 rows. This example shows that 36 ÷ 3 = 12.).

 motivation**math**™ LEVEL 4 ©2014 mentoring**minds**.com

1 Central City has a population of 36,473. Bridge City has a population of 102,785, and Smalltown has a population of 9,852. Estimate the total population of the three towns by rounding each population to the nearest thousand. Record your results below.

36,473 ⟶ _____

102,785 ⟶ _____

+   9,852 ⟶ _____

Estimated Total _____

2 Montrose Elementary School purchased 32 backpacks for $17 each. What is a reasonable estimate for the total cost of the backpacks?

Answer: _____

Explain how you found your estimate.

_____

_____

3 Heather spent $176 to purchase a total of 9 gifts for her nieces and nephews. If the gifts were equal in price, about how much did Heather spend on each gift?

Answer: _____

Explain how you found your estimate.

_____

_____

4 During the summer months, 6,398 people visit the Gateway Arch in St. Louis each day. If 6,398 is rounded to the nearest thousand, what is an estimate of how many people visit the Arch in seven days?

Answer: _____

Explain how you can make a closer estimate.

_____

_____

_____

Use the method you explained to estimate the total number of visitors in seven days.

Answer: _____

5 Gina's family went on vacation. They traveled 325 miles the first day, 481 miles the second day, and 119 miles the third day. Gina rounded the number for each day to the nearest hundred to estimate the total number of miles traveled. What was Gina's estimate?

Answer: _____

About how many more miles did the family travel the second day than the third day?

Answer: _____

Why does it make better sense to round the number of miles driven to the nearest hundred rather than the nearest thousand?

Answer: _____

_____

Unit 21 Guided Practice

1 For the school fund-raiser, Mrs. Day's class collected 4,864 pennies, and Miss Finley's class collected 2,342 pennies. Which is the best estimate of how many more pennies Mrs. Day's class collected than Miss Finley's class?

Ⓐ 3,000

Ⓑ 2,000

Ⓒ 5,000

Ⓓ 8,000

2 Mrs. Johnson purchased 5,498 pieces of candy for the fall carnival. She made treat bags for the students by placing 7 pieces of candy in each bag. To estimate the number of treat bags she made, Mrs. Johnson wrote 5,600 ÷ 7. Which best describes the method of estimation used by Mrs. Johnson?

Ⓕ Rounding the dividend to the nearest 10

Ⓖ Rounding the dividend to the nearest 100

Ⓗ Rounding the dividend to the nearest 1,000

Ⓙ Using compatible numbers

3 Martha rides 29 miles on her bicycle every day. About how many miles does Martha ride in 6 weeks?

Ⓐ 180 mi

Ⓑ 800 mi

Ⓒ 1,200 mi

Ⓓ 1,400 mi

4 Beth placed 386 pictures in a total of 5 photo albums. She placed about the same number of pictures in each album. Which is the best estimate of the total number of pictures Beth placed in each album?

Ⓕ 40

Ⓖ 60

Ⓗ 80

Ⓙ 100

5 Marissa collects coins. She has 1,501 U.S. coins and 985 coins from other countries. Marissa adds 2,000 and 1,000 to estimate how many coins she has in her collection. Is Marissa's estimate more or less than the actual number of coins?

Ⓐ More, because she rounds both numbers up

Ⓑ More, because she rounds one number down

Ⓒ Less, because she rounds both numbers up

Ⓓ Less, because she rounds one number down

6 Phillip plans to try out for the baseball team. He practiced at the batting cages for 12 days. He hit 48 balls each day. What is a reasonable estimate of the total number of balls Phillip hit during the 12 days?

Ⓕ 200

Ⓖ 400

Ⓗ 500

Ⓙ 700

motivation**math**™LEVEL 4

1 Three classes participated in a contest to see which class could read the most minutes. Ms. Busby's class read 12,580 minutes. Mr. Fulton's class read 14,609 minutes, and Mrs. Black's class read 9,772 minutes. If the numbers are rounded to the nearest thousand, about how many more minutes did Ms. Busby's class read than Mrs. Black's class?

Ⓐ 2,000 min   Ⓒ 3,000 min

Ⓑ 5,000 min   Ⓓ 22,000 min

2 Collin has 376 baseball cards, 223 football cards, and 204 basketball cards in his sports card collection. Which does **NOT** show a way to estimate the total number of sports cards in Collin's collection?

Ⓕ Round to the nearest 10 and add.
380 + 220 + 200 = 800

Ⓖ Round to the nearest 100 and add.
400 + 200 + 200 = 800

Ⓗ Use compatible numbers and add.
375 + 225 + 200 = 800

Ⓙ Add the numbers and round the sum.
376 + 223 + 204 = 803; 803 rounds to 800

3 Marvin ran for a total of 5,718 yards in 8 years as a professional football player. His yardage was close to the same number each year. Which expression best shows a way to use compatible numbers to estimate the approximate number of yards Marvin ran each year?

Ⓐ 5,600 ÷ 8 = 700

Ⓑ 6,000 × 8 = 48,000

Ⓒ 5,718 ÷ 8 = 714 r 6

Ⓓ 5,000 ÷ 8 = 625

4 Gia's family owns a peach orchard. Each summer, she places peaches in baskets to sell at the local farmer's market. In one day, Gia places 3 dozen peaches in each of 64 baskets. Which shows the best estimate of the number of peaches Gia packed that day?

Ⓕ 180   Ⓗ 1,800

Ⓖ 600   Ⓙ 2,400

5 Look at the group of numbers below.

7,843   7,285   7,967

Which statement about these numbers is **NOT** correct?

Ⓐ When rounded to the nearest ten, the estimated sum of the numbers is 23,100.

Ⓑ When rounded to the nearest hundred, the estimated sum of the numbers is 23,200.

Ⓒ When rounded to the nearest thousand, the estimated sum of the numbers is 23,000.

Ⓓ When rounded to the nearest hundred, the estimated difference between the first and third numbers is 200.

6 Mr. Braxton plants 18 trees in each row of his apple orchard. There are 28 rows in the orchard. About how many trees did Mr. Braxton plant?

Ⓕ Less than 300

Ⓖ Between 300 and 400

Ⓗ Between 400 and 500

Ⓙ More than 500

1 Each night last week, 298 people attended the musical at the local theater. Which is the best estimate of the total number of people who saw the musical last week?

Ⓐ 1,000

Ⓒ 1,800

Ⓑ 1,400

Ⓓ 2,100

2 Raj collects figurines. He has 479 Disney® figurines and 897 superhero figurines. Raj adds 500 and 900 to estimate the number of figurines in his collection. Is Raj's estimate more or less than the actual number of figurines?

Ⓕ Less, because he rounds both numbers up

Ⓖ Less, because he rounds one number down

Ⓗ More, because he rounds one number down

Ⓙ More, because he rounds both numbers up

3 A group of 64 students went on a field trip to the planetarium. Student tickets cost $18 each. Which is the best estimate for the total cost of the student tickets?

Ⓐ $640

Ⓒ $1,400

Ⓑ $1,200

Ⓓ $900

4 This fall, 156 students were selected for the dance team. If the teacher grouped the students into 4 equal groups, about how many students were in each group?

Ⓕ 40

Ⓗ 20

Ⓖ 30

Ⓙ 60

Use the table to answer questions 5 and 6.

The table shows how much money the Martinez family spent on a trip to New York City.

New York City Expenses

Item	Amount
Plane tickets	$1,790
Hotel rooms	$1,482
Meals	$1,045
Entertainment	$ 985

5 The family rounded each number to the nearest hundred to estimate the total expenses. Which best shows an estimate of the total amount of money spent by the Martinez family for the trip to New York City?

Ⓐ $6,000

Ⓑ $5,300

Ⓒ $4,500

Ⓓ $4,000

6 About how much more did the Martinez family spend on plane tickets than on hotel rooms?

Ⓕ $100

Ⓖ $200

Ⓗ $300

Ⓙ $400

motivation**math**™LEVEL 4

1 Mrs. Johnson asked her students to estimate the quotient of 6,348 ÷ 8.

- Matt said, "I will use compatible numbers to estimate." He recorded 6,400 ÷ 8 = 800.

- Jett said, "I will round both numbers and divide." She recorded 6,000 ÷ 10 = 600.

- Hugo said, "I will round and divide, but in a different way from Jett." He recorded 6,000 ÷ 8 = 750.

For this problem, which method of estimation do you think is the easiest to compute mentally? Why?

_____

_____

Which method gives you the best estimate for this problem? Justify your answer.

_____

_____

2 Create a graphic organizer that shows the likenesses and differences of estimation by rounding and estimation by using compatible numbers.

Journal

Monette estimated the quotient of 4,875 ÷ 7 by rounding the dividend to 4,900 and dividing by 7 for an estimate of 700. Why is it **NOT** necessary to round the divisor, 7, when estimating this quotient?

_____

_____

_____

_____

Vocabulary Activity

Compatible numbers are pairs of numbers that can be easily computed mentally. For example, 22 + 77 can be estimated using compatible numbers.

$$
\begin{array}{r}
22 \longrightarrow \quad 25 \\
+\ 77 \longrightarrow \quad 75 \\
\hline
100
\end{array}
$$

Using numbers as characters, create a cartoon that shows the meaning of compatible numbers.

Motivation Mike says, "Unbelievable work!"

Estimation Path

Tony needs to navigate his way through the number maze. Help Tony find his way by estimating the answer to each problem and shading each estimate, in order, on the maze. The answers will form the path from the start to the finish of the maze.

1. 6,385 ÷ 8	5. 57 + 28	9. 5 × 295	13. 28 × 42
2. 124 + 277	6. 83 − 37	10. 811 + 494	14. 357 ÷ 6
3. 195 − 98	7. 19 × 32	11. 88 − 37	15. 1,103 − 813
4. 4 × 397	8. 61 ÷ 2	12. 2,981 ÷ 6	16. 2,999 + 4,999

Start

800	5,000	200	9,000	2,300	3,000
400	100	10	7,000	2,400	20
2,700	1,600	90	40	1,900	2,200
80	1,000	1,800	600	1,700	6,000
4,000	2,600	1,500	30	1,100	2,500
2,100	70	1,300	700	60	300
2,000	1,400	50	500	1,200	8,000

Finish

1 A theater has 28 sections of seats. Each section has 48 seats. About how many seats does the theater have?

Answer: _____

2 The students at Appletree School raised money for new playground equipment. They have already raised $2,248 for the new equipment. The total cost of the new playground equipment is $7,526. About how much money do the students still need to raise for the equipment?

Answer: _____

Explain how you found the estimated answer.

_____

_____

3 Mr. Roy has $5,379 to divide equally among 6 savings accounts. About how much will he deposit in each savings account?

Answer: _____

Use the table below to answer questions 4 and 5.

The table below shows how many miles a pilot flew his airplane on 3 different days.

Miles Flown

Day	Number of Miles
Monday	4,862
Wednesday	3,137
Thursday	1,428

4 If each distance is rounded to the nearest thousand, about how many total miles did the pilot fly his airplane during these 3 days?

Answer: _____

5 If each distance is rounded to the nearest hundred, about how many more miles did the pilot fly on Monday than on Thursday?

Answer: _____

✂ -

Parent Activities

1. Work with your child to identify real-world situations in which estimating solutions is useful (e.g., determining about how many total cookies have been baked based on the rounded amount per tray, about how much the groceries will cost, about how many bracelets can be made based on the number of beads available). Help your child round and estimate the solutions to some of these problems as they are encountered in the real world.

2. Study grocery ads or catalogs with your child. Select 3 items and estimate the total cost of the items before tax.

1 A group of 6 friends baked a total of 5 dozen muffins. They divided the muffins equally. This equation can be used to find the number of muffins each friend received.

$$(5 \times 12) \div 6 = 10$$

Write a number in each section of the strip diagram to represent the equation.

12	12	12	12	120	= 60

10	10	10	10	10	10	= 60

2 Sal has 315 pieces of candy. He has 3 times as many pieces of candy as Joey. Write a multiplication equation that can be used to find j, the number of pieces of candy Joey has.

Equation: $j \times 3 = 315$

Write a related division equation that can be used to find j, the number of pieces of candy Joey has.

Equation: $315 \div 3 = j$

3 Carol baked chocolate chip cookies and oatmeal cookies for the school picnic. She baked 124 cookies altogether. There were 18 more chocolate chip cookies than oatmeal cookies. Carol created this strip diagram to represent the cookies.

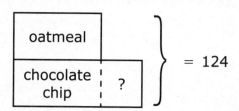

What is the missing value in Carol's strip diagram?

Answer: 18

Use the table to answer questions 4 and 5.

The Sluggo Bat Company makes baseball bats from different types of wood. The table below shows the prices of the bats.

Bat Prices

Type of Wood	Price
Oak	$86
Maple	$78
Ash	$55
Bamboo	$63

4 Coach Vega orders 30 bats for the team. He orders 7 oak bats, 7 maple bats, 12 ash bats, and some bamboo bats. Write an equation that can be used to find b, the number of bamboo bats Coach Vega orders.

Equation: $7 + 7 + 12 + b = 30$

How many bamboo bats does Coach Vega order?

Answer: 4 Bamboo bats

5 Complete this strip diagram to represent d, the difference in the total amounts Coach Vega spends for oak bats and maple bats.

Oak | $86 | $86 | $86 | $86 | $86 | $86 |

Maple | 78 | 78 | 78 | 78 | 78 | 78 | 78 |

d

602
544
56

What is the value of d?

Answer: $56.00

$56.00

1   Jazzy sells her old bike for $104 and some toys for $68. She uses the money to pay for 4 months of karate lessons. The cost of the lessons is the same each month. Which strip diagram shows Jazzy's cost for one month of karate lessons?

Ⓐ
104			
68	43	68	43

Ⓑ
104			
36	36	36	36

Ⓒ
104		68	
43	43	43	43

Ⓓ
104		43	
68	68	68	68

2   Joy baked 2 pizzas and cut each pizza into 8 slices. Joy and her brother ate all but 4 slices of the pizza. Which equation can be used to find s, the number of slices Joy and her brother ate?

Ⓕ $2 \times s = 8 \times 4$

Ⓖ $2 \times 8 + 4 = s$

Ⓗ $s = (2 + 8) - 4$

Ⓙ $8 \times 2 = s + 4$

3   The Salas family drove a total of 612 miles in 4 days. They drove equal distances on each of the first three days. On the fourth day, the family drove 180 miles. Which diagram shows the numbers of miles the family drove on each of the 4 days?

Ⓐ
144	144	144	180

Ⓑ
612	612	612	180

Ⓒ
180	180	180	612

Ⓓ
180	180	180	144

4   Which of the following word problems can be solved using the equation below?

$$(130 \times 4) + 26 + 14 = n$$

Ⓕ   Joe spent a total of $130 for 4 trees. He also bought bushes for $26 and $14. Find n, the total amount Joe spent for trees.

Ⓖ   Joe bought 4 trees for $130 each. He bought bushes for $26 and $14. Find n, the total amount Joe spent for trees and bushes.

Ⓗ   Joe spent a total of $130 for 4 trees and 2 bushes. He used coupons to save $26 on one bush and $14 on the other bush. Find n, the total amount Joe saved on bushes.

Ⓙ   Joe bought 4 trees for $130 each and a bush for $26. He used a coupon for $14 off his total purchase. Find n, the total amount Joe spent for plants.

5   Mr. Guerra and Ms. Faber have a total of 45 students in their classes. There are 3 more students in Ms. Faber's class than in Mr. Guerra's class. This diagram represents the numbers of students in the two classes.

Mr. G	
Ms. F	3

} = 45

Which equation can be used to find the number of students in Ms. Faber's class?

Ⓐ $(45 - 3) \div 2 = 21$

Ⓑ $(45 + 3) \times 2 = 96$

Ⓒ $(45 - 3) \times 2 = 42$

Ⓓ $(45 + 3) \div 2 = 24$

1 Rebecca had 1,040 stickers in her collection. She gave 41 stickers to Ana. She divided the remaining stickers equally among her 3 sisters. Which strip diagram could Rebecca use to find n, the number of stickers she gave each sister?

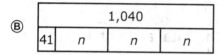

Ⓐ

1,040		41
n	n	n

Ⓑ

1,040			
41	n	n	n

Ⓒ

1,040	41
1,040	41	= n
1,040	41

Ⓓ

1,040		
n	41	41	41

2 Which of the following word problems could **NOT** be solved with this equation?

$$(158 + 417) \times 2 = m$$

Ⓕ Lea borrowed half of the marbles in Ted's collection. Lea borrowed 158 large marbles and 417 small marbles. Find m, the number of marbles in Ted's collection.

Ⓖ The school choir practiced 158 minutes in March and 417 minutes in April. In May, the choir practiced twice as many minutes as they practiced in March and April combined. Find m, the number of minutes the choir practiced in May.

Ⓗ Sam sold $158 in candy bars for a school fund-raiser. Stu sold twice as many candy bars as Sam. Altogether, they sold 417 candy bars. Find m, the number of candy bars Stu sold.

Ⓙ A monitor costs $158, and a computer costs $417. Sara and Leo each buy a monitor and a computer. Find m, the total amount Sara and Leo spend.

Use the table to answer questions 3 and 4.

Maddie, Shawn, and Pedro each buy tickets for a movie. They also buy 2 bags of popcorn and 1 box of candy. The table shows the prices at the theater.

Movie Theater Prices

Item	Price
Ticket	$8
Bag of popcorn	$6
Soda	$2
Box of candy	$3

3 Maddie buys 3 sodas. She pays with cash and receives $4 in change. Which equation can be used to find d, the number of dollars Maddie gives the snack bar worker?

Ⓐ $3 \times 2 = d - 4$

Ⓑ $d = (3 \times 2) - 4$

Ⓒ $d \times 3 \times 2 = 4$

Ⓓ $d - 2 = 3 \times 4$

4 The friends share the cost of the tickets, popcorn, and candy equally. Which strip diagram represents each friend's cost?

Ⓕ

8	6	3
Maddie	Shawn	Pedro

Ⓖ

8	8	8	6	6	3
Maddie		Shawn		Pedro	

Ⓗ

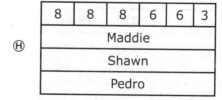

8	8	8	6	6	3
Maddie					
Shawn					
Pedro					

Ⓙ

8	8	8
Maddie	Shawn	Pedro

1 Jon watched a video that was 98 minutes long. Then he watched a TV show that was 17 minutes longer than the video. Jon used this diagram to calculate 213 minutes as the total combined length of both videos. Which is the missing value in Jon's diagram?

98	
?	17

$\left.\right\}$ = 213

Ⓐ 115   Ⓒ 98

Ⓑ 81   Ⓓ 396

2 Willow Bend Elementary has 214 girls and 232 boys. The school issues 4 textbooks to each student. Which equation can be used to find b, the total number of textbooks the school issues?

Ⓕ $214 \div 4 = 232 + b$

Ⓖ $214 + 232 = b \times 4$

Ⓗ $b = (214 + 232) \times 4$

Ⓙ $(214 + 232) \times b = 4$

3 Allie had 144 rocks in a collection. She gave 15 rocks to Stan. Then she lost 9 rocks. Allie divided the remaining rocks equally into 2 bags. She drew a strip diagram to find the number of rocks in each bag. Which could be Allie's diagram?

Ⓐ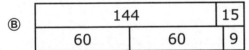

Ⓑ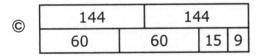

Ⓒ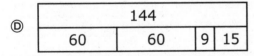

Ⓓ

144		
60	60	9	15

4 Principal Nelson purchased 15 dozen donuts for the teachers. She ate 2 donuts while she was setting out the food. Which equation can be used to find d, the number of donuts left for the teachers?

Ⓕ $15 \times 12 \times 2 = d$

Ⓖ $(15 \times 12) - 2 = d$

Ⓗ $(15 \times 12) + d = 2$

Ⓙ $d - (15 \times 12) = 2$

5 Which of the following problems could be solved with this strip diagram?

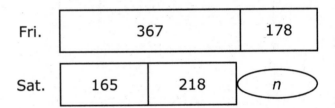

Fri.	367	178

Sat.	165	218	n

Ⓐ On Friday, 367 boys and 178 girls rode the Twister. On Saturday, 165 fewer boys and 218 fewer girls rode the Twister. Find n, the total number of children who rode the Twister on the two days.

Ⓑ On Friday, 367 boys and 178 girls rode the Twister. On Saturday, 165 boys and 218 girls rode the Twister. Find n, the difference between the total number of children who rode the Twister on Friday and Saturday.

Ⓒ On Friday, 367 boys and 178 girls rode the Twister. On Saturday, 165 more boys and 218 more girls rode the Twister than on Friday. Find n, the difference between the total number of children who rode the Twister on Friday and Saturday.

Ⓓ On Friday, 367 boys and 178 girls rode the Twister. On Saturday, 165 boys and 218 girls rode the Twister. Find n, the total number of boys and girls who rode the Twister on the two days.

1 Elaine opens her math book to a mystery page and challenges Tate with this math riddle.

- The mystery page is on the left.
- The sum of the 2 facing page numbers is 437.

Tate correctly uses the following equation to find p, the number of the mystery page.

$$p = (437 - 1) \div 2$$

Explain why Tate divided by 2 in the equation above.

_____

_____

Explain why Tate subtracted 1 from 437 in the equation above.

_____

_____

2 Write a word problem that could be solved with this strip diagram.

24	a		
32	32	32	

_____

_____

_____

_____

What is the solution to your problem?

Answer: $a =$ _____

Unit 23 Journal/Vocabulary Activity

Journal

Application
i
Apply

Give an example of a situation in everyday life in which you would need to perform several steps to find an unknown number.

_____

_____

_____

Vocabulary Activity

Study each equation and strip diagram. Then follow the guidelines below to finish the drawing.

$9 \times a = 81$	5 / 3 / 8	$14 - b = 7$	12 / 2 2 2 2 2 2

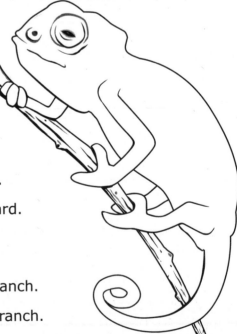

- If 9 is a product, draw a curled tongue.
- If 9 is a factor, draw a straight tongue.

- If 7 is a sum, color the lizard blue.
- If 8 is a sum, color the lizard yellow.

- If 12 is a divisor, color green dots on the lizard.
- If 12 is a dividend, color purple dots on the lizard.
- If 12 is a quotient, color red dots on the lizard.

- If 6 is an addend, draw brown leaves on the branch.
- If 3 is an addend, draw orange leaves on the branch.

Motivation Mike says, "Your work is first-rate!"

Rod Squad

Play *Rod Squad* in squads of 4-5 players each. Two squads compete against each other. Each squad needs a box of Cuisenaire® rods, 1 two-color counter, 1 game board, and a pencil and paper clip for the spinner. Each squad flips the counter and spins the spinner. The squad selects a rod color as indicated by the spinner. (The value of each rod color is indicated on the spinner.) If the counter lands on red, the squad takes any even number of rods. Otherwise, the squad takes any odd number of rods. Squads repeat the process in turn until each squad has taken a set that includes 4 different rod colors. Squads model a multi-step equation using only the set of selected rods. Models do not have to include all rods in the set. Once a model has been created, a squad member draws a strip diagram. Another squad member records an equation for the diagram. The squad then uses the same set of rods to create a different model, diagram, and equation. Play continues until one squad completes each section of the table or until the teacher calls time. The winner is the squad with more correct pairs of diagrams and equations. Additional models may be recorded on a separate sheet of paper if needed.

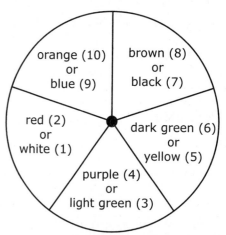

Strip Diagram	Equation
Example <table><tr><td colspan="2">10</td><td>4</td></tr><tr><td>7</td><td colspan="2">7</td></tr></table>	$(10 + 4) \div 2 = n$ $7 = n$

1 For his birthday, Rex received 6 gift cards worth $25 each. He also received some cash. Altogether, Rex received a total of $194 in gift cards and cash. Write an equation that can be used to find *c*, the amount of cash Rex received.

Equation: _____

2 The dentist cleans April's teeth for $65. He takes x-rays for $51 and fills a cavity for $130. April plans to pay her dental bill in 3 equal payments. She uses this equation to find the amount of each payment.

$$(65 + 51 + 130) \div 3 = 82$$

Record a number in each section of the strip diagram below to represent April's equation.

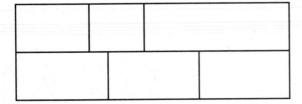

3 While Steven was at summer camp, he wrote 5 letters to his mom and 3 letters to his best friend. Ty wrote 4 times as many letters as Steven. In the space below, create a strip diagram that can be used to find *t*, the number of letters Ty wrote.

4 A farmer places 2 scarecrows of different heights to guard a total of 292 tomato plants. The taller scarecrow guards 28 more tomato plants than the shorter scarecrow. Record a number or letter in each empty space on this diagram to show how the farmer could find *p*, the number of tomato plants the shorter scarecrow guards.

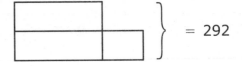

Record an equation to match your diagram.

Equation: _____

Parent Activities

1. Play a game in which your family creates a run-on story. The first person makes a statement that includes a number (e.g., 18 squirrels live in a tree.). The next person adds a statement to the story (e.g., Each squirrel throws 16 acorns every day.). Continue until all family members have a turn. The last family member must ask a question (e.g., How many acorns did the squirrels throw in a week?). Record an equation that represents the run-on story (e.g., 18 x 16 x 7 = c).

2. Give your child 3 or more activities to perform in order (e.g., collect the mail, take out the trash, and feed the dog). Praise your child for performing the activities in order, with attention to every step. Your child is now learning to complete math problems with more than one step. Help your child become accustomed to following multiple steps. This sets the groundwork for success in the math classroom.

1 Ms. Lu placed 3 beans in a jar each time her class received a compliment. The class wrote this rule to show how to find the number of beans placed in the jar.

compliments × 3 = number of beans

The class began an input-output table for the rule. Record an expression and the number of beans for 2 and 3 compliments to complete the table.

Daily Compliments

Number of Compliments	Expression	Beans in Jar
1	1 × 3	3
2		
3		

How many beans did Ms. Lu's class receive for 19 compliments?

Answer: _____

2 Greg creates this pattern rule.

$$\triangle \div 8 = \diamondsuit$$

Use Greg's rule to complete the table.

Greg's Pattern

△	Expression	◇
3,408	3,408 ÷ 8	
3,416		
3,424		

If △ = 400, then ◇ = _____.

If ◇ = 25, then △ = _____.

3 Mason begins a new exercise program. He wants to increase the number of sit-ups he completes each day. Mason writes this rule to show the relationship between the number of days he exercises and the number of sit-ups he plans to do each day.

number of days + 4 = number of sit-ups

Finish the table to match Mason's rule.

Mason's Sit-ups

Number of Days	1	3	5
Expression			
Number of Sit-ups			

4 Jenna and her brother Cleo write math facts for homework every night. Because she is younger, Jenna always writes 5 fewer facts than Cleo. Jenna creates an input-output table to show the relationship between the numbers of facts she and Cleo write each night. Record the missing expressions and output values on Jenna's table.

Math Facts

Cleo's Facts (Input)	Expression	Jenna's Facts (Output)
10		
11		
12		

Write an expression that can be used to find the number of math facts Jenna writes if Cleo writes 31 facts. Then, solve the expression to find the answer.

Expression: _____

Answer: _____

Use the information to answer questions 1–3.

Delsey's dad gives her permission to download songs on the computer. Each song takes 27 seconds to download. Delsey begins this table to show the relationship between the number of songs and the time needed for downloads.

Download Times

Number of Songs (Input)	Numerical Expression	Number of Seconds (Output)
1		
2		
3		
4		

1 Which numerical expression should Delsey record for 3 songs?

Ⓐ 3 + 27   Ⓒ 3 × 27

Ⓑ 27 ÷ 3   Ⓓ 27 − 3

2 How many seconds will it take Delsey to download 4 songs?

Ⓕ 98 seconds   Ⓗ 31 seconds

Ⓖ 104 seconds   Ⓙ 108 seconds

3 Delsey extends the table. Which pair of input and output values could **NOT** appear in Delsey's extended table?

Ⓐ Input: 12
Output: 324

Ⓑ Input: 20
Output: 504

Ⓒ Input: 21
Output: 567

Ⓓ Input: 18
Output: 486

4 Ms. Green's art students need colored pencils for a project. She writes this rule to show the relationship between the number of colored pencils available and the number of students who can complete the project.

number of pencils ÷ 3 = number of students

Ms. Green creates an input-output table in which the input value is the number of colored pencils available and the output value is the number of students. Which could be Ms. Green's table?

Ⓕ

Input	Output
36	39
33	36
30	33

Ⓖ

Input	Output
3	9
4	12
5	15

Ⓗ

Input	Output
48	16
45	15
42	14

Ⓙ

Input	Output
96	32
95	29
94	26

1 Sheena buys 1,000 stickers. She plans to share 15 stickers with each of her friends. Sheena creates this table to show the relationship between the number of friends who will receive stickers and the total number of stickers she will share.

Sheena's Stickers

Number of Friends (Input)	1	2	3	4
Stickers Shared (Output)	15	30	45	60

If this pattern continues, how many total stickers will Sheena share with 47 friends?

Ⓐ 750   Ⓒ 282

Ⓑ 62   Ⓓ 705

2 Ken's dad gives him different amounts of money each week for completing chores. Ken also receives $2 each week as a gift from his aunt. Ken records this rule to find his total weekly income for different amounts of chore money.

chore money + $2 = total income

Which pair of input and output values does **NOT** match Ken's rule?

Ⓕ Input: $19
    Output: $21

Ⓖ Input: $14
    Output: $28

Ⓗ Input: $26
    Output: $28

Ⓙ Input: $ 8
    Output: $10

Use the information to answer questions 3–5.

Mara plays soccer and basketball every afternoon. She always spends 8 fewer minutes playing basketball than soccer. Mara begins this table to show the pattern in the numbers of minutes she plays basketball for several different soccer times.

Mara's Times

Soccer (Minutes)	Numerical Expression	Basketball (Minutes)
60		
55		
50		

3 Which numerical expression should Mara record for a soccer time of 50 minutes?

Ⓐ 50 − 8   Ⓒ 58 + 8

Ⓑ 50 + 8   Ⓓ 50 × 8

4 If Mara spends 22 minutes playing soccer, how many minutes will she spend playing basketball?

Ⓕ 14 minutes   Ⓗ 30 minutes

Ⓖ 52 minutes   Ⓙ 24 minutes

5 Which pair of values fits Mara's pattern?

Ⓐ Soccer time: 60 minutes
    Basketball time: 68 minutes

Ⓑ Soccer time: 55 minutes
    Basketball time: 49 minutes

Ⓒ Soccer time: 45 minutes
    Basketball time: 37 minutes

Ⓓ Not here

1   Jamar has a new baby sister, Mandy. Jamar writes this rule to show the pattern in his and Mandy's ages.

Jamar's age − 9 = Mandy's age

Which input-output table matches Jamar's rule?

Ⓐ

Jamar's Age (years)	Mandy's Age (years)
19	26
34	41
46	52

Ⓑ

Jamar's Age (years)	Mandy's Age (years)
3	6
4	5
5	4

Ⓒ

Jamar's Age (years)	Mandy's Age (years)
16	7
26	17
46	27

Ⓓ

Jamar's Age (years)	Mandy's Age (years)
13	4
59	50
62	53

Use the information to answer questions 2–4.

Jesse records a pattern rule.

$$\bigcirc \div 6 = \langle\!\rangle$$

He creates this input-output table for the rule.

Jesse's Rule

◯ (Input)	Numerical Expression	⬡ (Output)
390		
396		
402		
408		

2   Which numerical expression should Jesse record for an input value of 408?

Ⓕ   408 ÷ 6   Ⓗ   408 ÷ 4

Ⓖ   408 × 4   Ⓙ   6 ÷ 408

3   What is the output value for an input value of 402?

Ⓐ   70   Ⓒ   67

Ⓑ   66   Ⓓ   72

4   Jesse extends the pattern in the table. Which pair of input and output values could **NOT** be recorded on Jesse's extended table?

Ⓕ   Input: 534   Ⓗ   Input: 642
    Output: 89   Output: 107

Ⓖ   Input: 663   Ⓙ   Input: 294
    Output: 102   Output: 49

Princess Stella was celebrating a special occasion. It was 7 days before her seventh birthday! Her father, King Leo, loved math problems, so he gave Stella a choice of gifts as listed below. King Leo told Princess Stella that she must choose one of the gifts.

Gift 1: Stella could receive 70 gold coins each day for the 7 days leading to her birthday.

Gift 2: Stella could receive 7 gold coins on day 1, double that amount on day 2, double the day 2 amount for day 3, and continue the pattern of doubling through the 7 days.

If you were Princess Stella, which gift would you choose? Why?

_____

_____

Complete the tables to show how many gold coins Stella would receive each day.

Gift 1: Number of Coins

Day	Number of Coins
1	
2	
3	
4	
5	
6	
7	

Gift 2: Number of Coins

Day	Number of Coins
1	
2	
3	
4	
5	
6	
7	

What is the total number of coins Stella receives with Gift 1? Show all work.

What is the total number of coins Stella receives with Gift 2? Show all work.

Unit 24 Journal/Vocabulary Activity

Standard 4.5(B) – Readiness

Journal

Provide a title for this input-output table. Then write and solve a word problem based on information in the table.

Input	1	2	3	4	5
Expression	1 × 12	2 × 12	3 × 12	4 × 12	5 × 12
Output					

_____

_____

_____

_____

Vocabulary Activity

Evaluate each expression on these input-output tables. Then answer the questions.

Table A

Input △	Expression	Output ☐
1	1 × 1	
2	2 × 1	
3	3 × 1	

Table B

Input △	Expression	Output ☐
1	1 + 1	
2	2 + 1	
3	3 + 1	

What is the rule for each table?

Table A: _____   **Table B:** _____

On Table B, what are the output values for the input values of 5, 6, and 7?

Answers: _____, _____, _____

Motivation Molly says, "Way to go!"

Digit Dog

Play *Digit Dog* with a partner. Each player needs 1 game board, a pencil, and 2 dice. Player 1 chooses to roll 1 or 2 dice. Player 1 records the total number of dots inside an empty box in one of the tables. If the player records the number in an incorrect box, he/she erases the number. If the player rolls a number that cannot be recorded in an empty box, the player skips the turn. Play passes to player 2, and the players alternate turns. The winner is the first player to correctly complete every table on his/her game board.

Input	Numerical Expression	Output
1	☐ × 1	3
2	3 × ☐	☐
☐	3 × 3	☐
4	3 × ☐	12
5	3 × ☐	15
6	☐ × 6	18

Rule: Divide by 2	
Input	Output
16	☐
18	9
20	☐
22	☐
24	☐

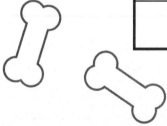

Input	Numerical Expression	Output
6	2 × 6	☐
7	2 × ☐	14
☐	2 × 8	16
☐	2 × 9	18

Unit 24 Homework

1   Complete the input-output table below to show the following relationship.

input value + 999 = output value

Input-Output Table

Input	1	2	3	4	5
Expression	1 + 999	2 + 999			
Output	1,000				

2   Noelle is unpacking boxes of tree ornaments from the attic. To find the total number of ornaments, she multiplies the number of boxes by 12. Noelle begins this table to calculate the number of ornaments for different numbers of boxes. Complete Noelle's table by recording an expression or number in each empty space.

Tree Ornaments

Number of Boxes	Expression	Number of Ornaments
4	4 × 12	
5		
6		
7		

What expression and number of ornaments should Noelle record for 9 boxes?

Expression: _____

Answer: _____

3   Gavin makes punch for a party. He divides the number of guests by 2 to find the number of scoops of drink mix needed. Gavin uses this input-output table to find the number of scoops of drink mix needed for different numbers of guests. Complete Gavin's table by recording expressions and output values.

Punch for Party

Guests	10	20	30
Expression			
Scoops of Drink Mix			

According to the pattern in Gavin's table, how many scoops of drink mix are needed for 106 guests?

Answer: _____

If Gavin uses 38 scoops of drink mix, how many guests will he serve?

Answer: _____

✂ -

Parent Activities

1. Create a table to show the pattern in the cost of multiple numbers of an item. Use the pattern to predict how much 25 items would cost.

2. Encourage your child to create patterns for you to extend.

1 Makesha's rectangular tabletop is 5 feet long and 3 feet wide as shown by the model.

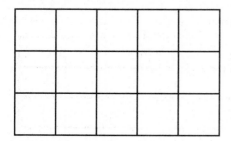

What is the perimeter of Makesha's tabletop?

Answer: _____

What is the area of Makesha's tabletop?

Answer: _____

2 Mr. Carlson wants to carpet the family room of his house as shown in the diagram. He multiplied 10 × 14 to determine how much carpet to purchase.

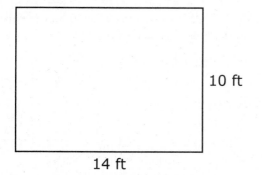

10 ft

14 ft

Why did Mr. Carlson multiply 10 × 14?

Answer: _____

_____

_____

3 Nachele measures her rectangular bedroom ceiling and buys exactly 48 feet of wallpaper border to put around the ceiling. If the length of Nachele's ceiling is 14 feet, what is the width?

Answer: _____

Explain how you found your answer.

_____

_____

4 Trevor folds a square sheet of paper in half vertically. He then folds the paper in half horizontally to form 4 congruent squares. The model below represents the paper.

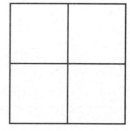

The perimeter of each small square is 48 centimeters. What is the perimeter of Trevor's original sheet of paper?

Answer: _____

Explain how you found your answer.

_____

_____

_____

Write and solve an equation to find the area of Trevor's original sheet of paper.

Answer: _____

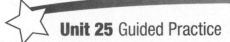
1 Mr. Edison asks his students to design a rectangular garden with a perimeter of 12 units. Which design does **NOT** show a garden with a perimeter of 12 units?

Ⓐ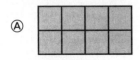

Ⓑ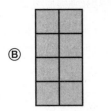

Ⓒ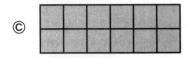

Ⓓ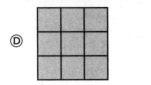

2 Every evening, Candy jogs around her neighborhood. The block she jogs around is in the shape of a square.

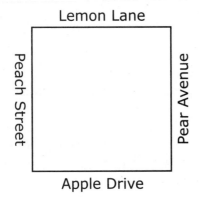

What formula can Candy use to determine how far she jogs each evening?

Ⓕ $P = 4 \times s$ Ⓗ $P = 2 \times s$

Ⓖ $A = s \times s$ Ⓙ $A = l \times w$

3 City Park has a children's wading pool that is surrounded by a rectangular fence. The diagram shows the pool and the fence.

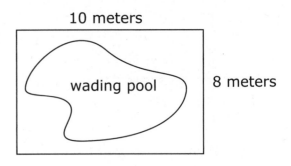

Which of the following is a true statement about the area of the wading pool?

Ⓐ The area of the wading pool is equal to 80 square meters.

Ⓑ The area of the wading pool is less than 80 square meters.

Ⓒ The area of the wading pool is equal to 36 meters.

Ⓓ The area of the wading pool is greater than 80 square meters.

4 Mr. Schilling owns a construction company. He pours a concrete patio that is 54 feet long and 18 feet wide.

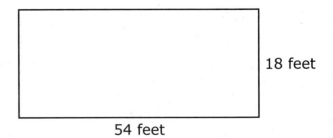

Mr. Schilling pays for concrete by the number of square feet. What is the area of the patio he pours?

Ⓕ 144 sq ft   Ⓗ 942 sq ft

Ⓖ 972 sq ft   Ⓙ 486 sq ft

1 Butch has a square closet in his bedroom. He wants to find the area of the floor of the closet. He measures the length of one side of the floor. What other measurement does Butch need to find the area of the closet floor?

Ⓐ The width of the closet

Ⓑ The height of the closet

Ⓒ The depth of the closet

Ⓓ He does not need any other measurement.

2 Mrs. Able bought a rectangular rug. The rug has an area of 48 square feet. Which of the following could **NOT** be the dimensions of Mrs. Able's new rug?

Ⓕ Length = 16 feet, Width = 3 feet

Ⓖ Length = 12 feet, Width = 4 feet

Ⓗ Length = 8 feet, Width = 6 feet

Ⓙ Length = 9 feet, Width = 5 feet

3 Mrs. Gardner is paving the sidewalk in front of her home with square tiles. The perimeter of each tile is 40 inches. Which pair of equations can be used to find the area of each tile in square inches?

Ⓐ $40 \div 4 = 10$, and $10 + 10 = 20$

Ⓑ $40 \times 4 = 160$, and $160 \times 10 = 1,600$

Ⓒ $40 \div 4 = 10$, and $10 \times 10 = 100$

Ⓓ $40 + 4 = 44$, and $44 \div 4 = 11$

4 Melinda has a rectangular flower garden. The width of her garden is 5 feet. Melinda uses 60 feet of edging to go around the garden. What is the length, in feet, of Melinda's garden?

Record your answer and fill in the bubbles on the grid below. Be sure to use the correct place value.

				•		
⓪	⓪	⓪	⓪		⓪	⓪
①	①	①	①		①	①
②	②	②	②		②	②
③	③	③	③		③	③
④	④	④	④		④	④
⑤	⑤	⑤	⑤		⑤	⑤
⑥	⑥	⑥	⑥		⑥	⑥
⑦	⑦	⑦	⑦		⑦	⑦
⑧	⑧	⑧	⑧		⑧	⑧
⑨	⑨	⑨	⑨		⑨	⑨

5 Brad's family is building a new house. The carpenter allowed Brad to help him calculate the length of baseboard needed to go around the bases of the walls in the dining room. This figure shows Brad's dining room.

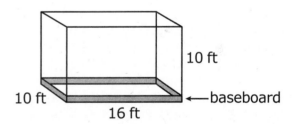

Which of the following expressions could be used to find the total length, in feet, of baseboard needed?

Ⓐ 10×16

Ⓑ $(2 \times 10) + (2 \times 16)$

Ⓒ $16 \times 10 \times 10$

Ⓓ $10 \times (16 + 10)$

1 Travis built a stage for the Summer Theater Company. The area of the stage is 720 square feet.

720 square feet

Which could be the dimensions of the stage?

Ⓐ Length 40 Width 19

© Length 35 Width 15

Ⓑ Length 36 Width 20

Ⓓ Length 35 Width 21

2 Ali bought 2 picture frames. The rectangles represent the sizes of the frames.

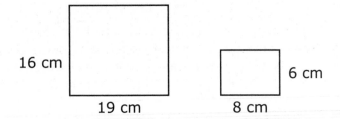

16 cm

19 cm

6 cm

8 cm

What is the difference, in square centimeters, between the areas of the two picture frames?

Record your answer and fill in the bubbles on the grid below. Be sure to use the correct place value.

3 Shelby's parents want to place a fence around a new dog pen in the backyard. The length of the pen is 17 feet, and the width is 15 feet. How many feet of fencing do they need to buy?

Ⓐ 64 feet

© 255 feet

Ⓑ 32 feet

Ⓓ 510 feet

4 Which equation **CANNOT** be used to determine the perimeter of the square below?

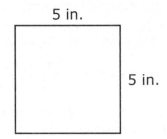

5 in.

5 in.

Ⓕ $4 \times 5 = P$

Ⓖ $5 + 5 + 5 + 5 = P$

Ⓗ $(2 \times 5) + (2 \times 5) = P$

Ⓙ $5 \times 5 = P$

5 The framed painting in Ping's room has dimensions of 16 inches wide and 20 inches long. Ping took the painting down and replaced it with a framed painting that is 1 inch longer and 1 inch wider than the old one. What is the area of the new painting?

Ⓐ 896 square inches

Ⓑ 357 square inches

© 120 square inches

Ⓓ 74 square inches

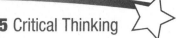

1 Dell, Anna, Mason, and Jenna each have their own bedroom. The floor of each bedroom has a different area. The areas are 120 square feet, 121 square feet, 128 square feet, and 132 square feet. Use the clues below to determine which bedroom belongs to each child.

- Mason's bedroom floor is a perfect square.

- Anna's bedroom floor has the same width as Mason's, but its length is longer.

- Jenna's floor has a length that is twice its width and a perimeter of 48 feet.

- The width of Dell's bedroom floor is 1 foot less than the width of Mason's floor, and the length is the same as the length of Anna's floor.

Complete the table to show which bedroom belongs to each child, and record the dimensions of the rooms.

Bedroom Dimensions

Child	Area	Length	Width
Dell			
Anna			
Mason			
Jenna			

2 Mrs. Davis plans for 2 fourth-grade classes to watch a movie. She arranges 39 carpet squares so that every student has one carpet square to sit on while watching the movie. After Mrs. Davis arranges the carpet squares, Maria counts to find that the perimeter of the sitting area is 32 units. In the space below, draw a diagram to show how the carpet square arrangement might look.

Unit 25 Journal/Vocabulary Activity

Journal

Think about what you know about the perimeter and area of a rectangle. Draw all possible rectangles with an area of 36 square units. Label the lengths and widths of the rectangles, then find the perimeter of each rectangle.

What generalization can you make about the perimeters of rectangles in relation to the shapes of the rectangles (long and thin versus square)?

_____

_____

_____

_____

Vocabulary Activity

Work in groups of 3-5. Write the vocabulary words from the word bank on index cards. Shuffle the cards and place them face down in the middle of the group.

Word Bank		
area	length	side
dimension	perimeter	square
formula	rectangle	square unit
		width

Spinner:
- Use motions or gestures.
- Draw a picture.
- Use words to describe.

In turn, each player selects the top card and, using a pencil and paper clip, spins the spinner. The player must use the method shown on the spinner to try to get the other players in the group to say the word. The first player to state the correct word scores 1 point, and the person giving the clues scores 1 point. When all words have been used, the cards may be reshuffled, and the game may be replayed.

motivation**math**™LEVEL 4   ©2014 mentoring**minds**.com

Motivation Mike says, "You've outdone yourself!"

Capture the Block

Play *Capture the Block* with a partner. Each player uses a different color to create rectangular blocks on the game board. In turn, players roll two dice. The product of the numbers rolled indicates the number of line segments a player may draw to try to create a rectangular block. For example, if a player rolls 4 and 6, the player marks 24 line segments on the game board. The player may choose to draw a closed figure with a perimeter of 24 units, or the player may choose to simply mark 24 units of a larger block, hoping to complete the block on another turn. The player who closes any rectangular block is the one who captures the block. Blocks created must include whole squares only (no diagonals). When a player closes a block, he/she colors the area and records both the area and perimeter in the space. The winner is the player with the greatest total area.

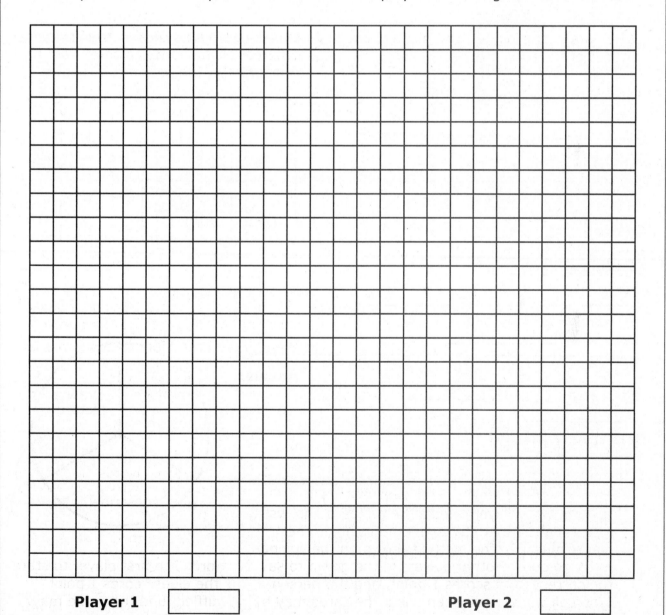

Player 1 [　　　　　]　　　　　**Player 2** [　　　　　]

1 Carmen plans to put plastic edging around a rectangular flower bed. The width of the flower bed is 12 feet, and the length is twice the width. What is the perimeter of Carmen's flower bed?

Answer: _____

Carmen decides to spread fertilizer over the top of the flower bed. She purchases a bag of fertilizer.

FERTILIZER
Covers 250 square feet

Will Carmen have enough fertilizer for the flower bed?

Answer: _____

Explain your answer.

_____

_____

_____

2 Several Olympic sports are played on indoor courts. The table shows three Olympic sports and the dimensions, in feet, of the rectangular courts on which they are played. Find the areas and perimeters of the courts.

Sport	l	w	P	A
Basketball	28	15		
Volleyball	18	9		
Badminton	13	6		

3 Liam's dad built a deck in the backyard. The rest of the yard is planted with grass. A diagram of the backyard is shown.

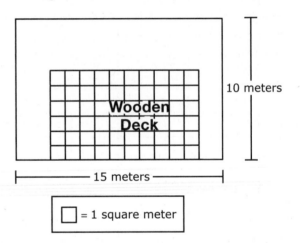

Wooden Deck

10 meters

← 15 meters →

☐ = 1 square meter

What is the area planted with grass?

Answer: _____

Parent Activities

1. Use small square crackers (e.g., saltines, graham crackers, etc.) to create a rectangle. Work with your child to identify the perimeter of the cracker rectangle. Have your child draw the rectangle on paper and record the perimeter and area. Then challenge your child to make and record as many rectangles as possible with the same perimeter but different areas. Repeat the activity and find rectangles with the same area but different perimeters.

2. Have your child use a measuring tape to find the lengths and widths of rectangular rooms in the house to the nearest whole foot. Use the dimensions to find the perimeter of each floor by adding the lengths. Use the dimensions to find the area of each floor by multiplying the length and width.

1 Sort the letters of the alphabet shown below according to the number of lines of symmetry. Record the answers in the table.

A B C D E F G H I J K L M N O P Q R S T U V W X Y Z

0 lines of symmetry												
1 line of symmetry												
2 or more lines of symmetry												

Create words using the rules in the table.

Symmetry Words

Create words using only letters that have at least 1 line of symmetry.	Create words using only letters that have exactly 1 line of symmetry.	Create words using letters that have 2 or more lines of symmetry.

2 A regular polygon is a polygon that has all sides and angles of equal measure. Five regular polygons are shown on the table. Draw all possible lines of symmetry on each polygon. Then, write the total number of lines of symmetry in the box beneath each figure.

	Triangle	Square	Pentagon	Hexagon	Octagon
Regular Polygon	△	□	⬠	⬡	⯃
Number of Lines of Symmetry					

What generalization can you make about the relationship between the number of sides on a regular polygon and the number of lines of symmetry?

_____

Unit 27 Journal/Vocabulary Activity

Journal

Your younger brother hears you tell your parents that you are studying symmetry in mathematics. He asks you what symmetry is. How would you explain lines of symmetry to your brother? Use words and pictures to show your answer.

_____

_____

_____

_____

Vocabulary Activity

Use words and pictures to complete the word map below for the word *symmetry*.

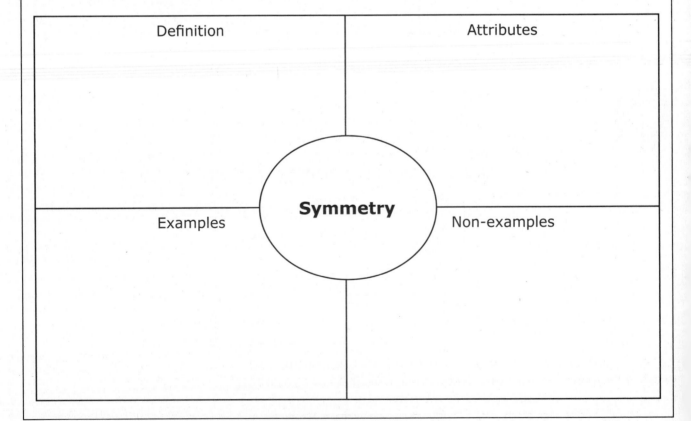

Definition

Attributes

Examples

Symmetry

Non-examples

motivation**math**™ LEVEL 4

1 When a capital letter A is printed, a triangle is formed. Different letter styles may result in different types of triangles in the letter A. In the chart below, trace each letter A and notice the type of triangle that is formed. Identify the type of triangle based on the angles in the letter.

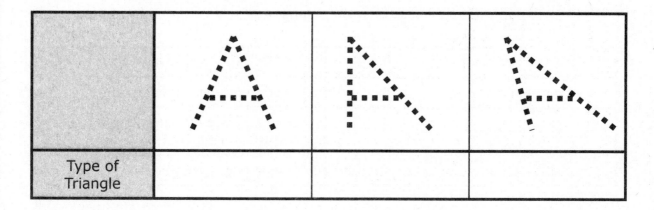

Type of Triangle			

The line segments form a right triangle in this numeral: 4

In the space below, sketch the numeral 4 to show an acute triangle and an obtuse triangle.

2 Based on your knowledge of the prefix *tri-*, what does *triangle* mean?

_____

_____

_____

Create two new words that begin with the prefix *tri-*. Write your new words and their meanings.

_____

_____

_____

Unit 28 Journal/Vocabulary Activity

Journal

The words *acute* and *obtuse* are multiple-meaning words. The mathematical meanings of these words are:

acute — measuring less than a right angle

obtuse — measuring more than a right angle

The words *acute* and *obtuse* have other meanings.

Acute	Obtuse
1. developing quickly	1. slow to learn or understand
2. severe or intense	2. a sound or sensation that is not easily heard or felt
3. sensitive to sound or other stimulus	3. a leaf with a rounded or blunt tip

For each sentence below, decide which meaning is used for the word *acute* or *obtuse*. On the line before each sentence, write the number of the meaning.

_____ When I didn't understand what my sister was explaining, she said, "You are so obtuse!"

_____ Mom said she had an acute headache, so she took two aspirin and went to bed.

_____ The obtuse leaves of the prickly pear cactus are edible.

_____ Bloodhound dogs are known to have an acute sense of smell.

_____ I had to strain to hear the soft, obtuse sounds of bells in the distance.

_____ The hospital reported an acute flu epidemic in our city.

Vocabulary Activity

Record the number of each triangle in the appropriate section of the chart.

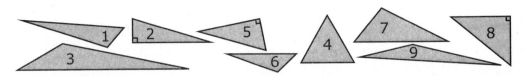

Acute triangles	Right triangles	Obtuse triangles

Motivation Molly says, "Your hard work is paying off!"

Triangles Galore

In the space below, draw multiple line segments to divide the area inside the frame into triangles of different sizes. After the area is divided into triangles, color the triangles according to the key.

Color acute triangles blue.

Color right triangles red.

Color obtuse triangles green.

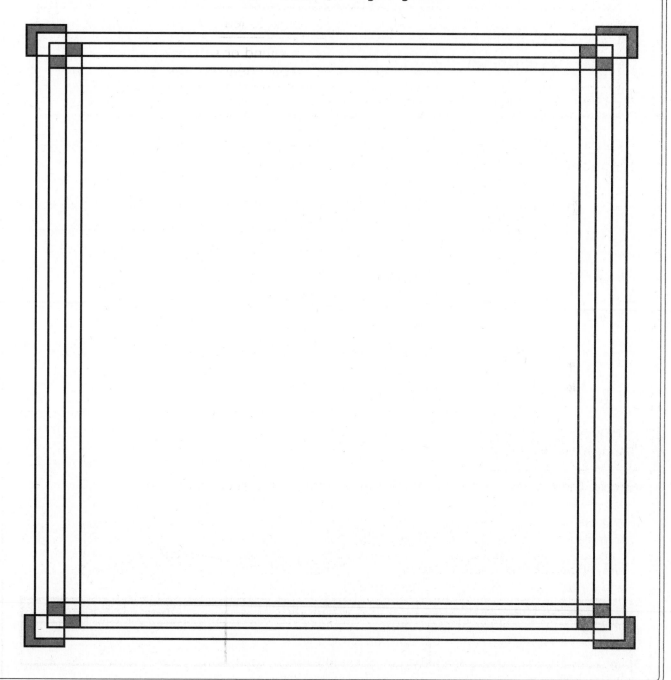

Each protractor below has one line drawn on it. Draw the other two lines to complete the triangle.

1 The protractor shows one line segment of an acute triangle. Draw two additional line segments to complete the acute triangle.

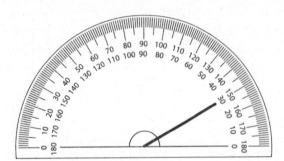

3 The protractor shows one line segment of an obtuse triangle. Draw two additional line segments to complete the obtuse triangle.

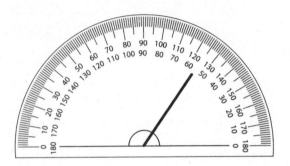

2 The protractor shows one line segment of a right triangle. Draw two additional line segments to complete the right triangle.

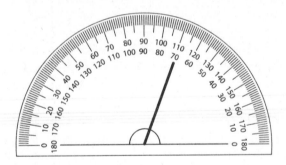

4 Explain the difference between these three types of triangles.

_____

_____

_____

_____

_____

✂ -

Parent Activities

1. Use miniature marshmallows and small pretzel sticks to create and discuss triangles with your child. Use the pretzels as sides (break pretzels as necessary to adjust the size) and marshmallows as vertices. Build acute triangles (triangles with all angles less than 90°), right triangles (triangles with one angle measuring exactly 90°), and obtuse triangles (triangles with one angle measuring more than 90°).

2. Use a piece of yarn, a shoelace, a jump rope, or a similar object to create triangles with your child. Then use a sheet of paper or other item with square corners to identify the triangles as acute, obtuse, or right based on the measures of the angles.

3. Look for triangles in the real world (e.g., on billboards, road signs, on food containers, in magazines, etc.). Have your child identify the triangles as acute, obtuse, or right.

Name _____

1 Label each statement as possible (*P*) or not possible (*N*). Draw a picture to the right of each statement to justify your answers.

_____ A trapezoid with 2 right angles

_____ An obtuse triangle with 2 obtuse angles

_____ A rhombus with 4 right angles

2 Sort these figures by sketching them on the Venn diagram. Label the ovals on the Venn diagram with the attributes you used for your sort.

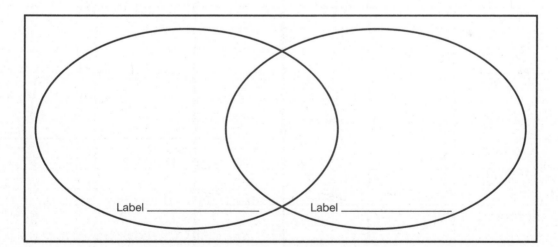

Label _____   Label _____

Explain how you sorted the figures.

_____

_____

Unit 29 Journal/Vocabulary Activity

Journal

Mr. Diboll told his students, "Every rectangle is a parallelogram, but not every parallelogram is a rectangle."

Use pictures and words to explain what Mr. Diboll meant.

_____

_____

Vocabulary Activity

Complete the table to show the attributes of each polygon pictured.

Polygon	Number of right angles	Number of acute angles	Number of obtuse angles	Pairs of parallel sides	Pairs of perpendicular sides
Trapezoid					
Parallelogram					
Rectangle					
Rhombus					
Hexagon					

motivation**math**™LEVEL 4

Motivation Mike says, "You came through!"

Connect Three

Play *Connect Three* with a partner. Each pair of players needs a game board and a paper clip and pencil for the spinners. Each player needs a different color pencil or marker. In turn, players spin the two spinners to identify an attribute and a two-dimensional shape. On any open block on the board, the player sketches the given shape with at least one example of the specified attribute. For example, if the player spins *acute angle* and *triangle*, he/she draws a triangle with at least one acute angle. If the player spins an attribute and shape combination that is not possible (such as *parallel sides* and *triangle*), the player skips that turn. The winner is the first player to claim four blocks in a row horizontally, vertically, or diagonally.

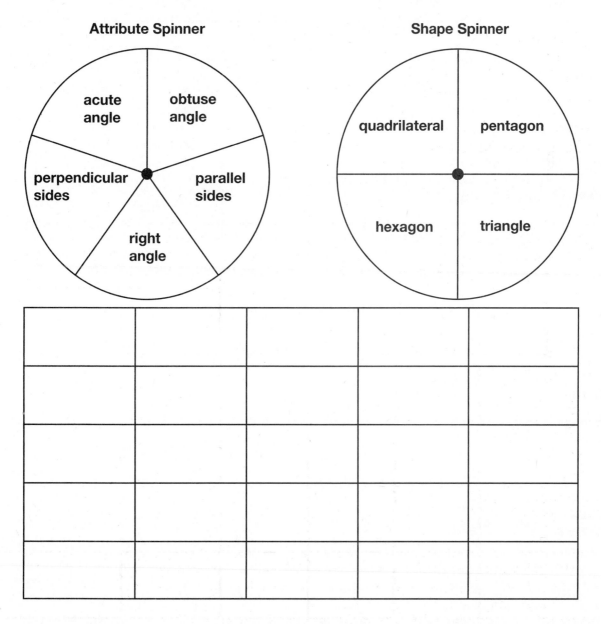

Attribute Spinner

acute angle
obtuse angle
perpendicular sides
parallel sides
right angle

Shape Spinner

quadrilateral
pentagon
hexagon
triangle

1   The triangles in this set share a common attribute.

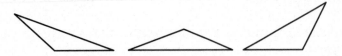

Use a ruler to draw another triangle that belongs in the set.

What name describes the 4 triangles above?

Answer: _____

2   Use a ruler to draw a quadrilateral that has 2 acute angles, 2 obtuse angles, and 2 pairs of parallel sides.

What name best describes your quadrilateral?

Answer: _____

3   A parallelogram is a quadrilateral with 2 pairs of parallel sides. Circle the name of each figure that is always a parallelogram.

trapezoid   rectangle   square

rhombus   hexagon

4   Cedric drew this sketch in art class.

Cedric says that his sketch is in the shape of a rectangle. Is Cedric correct?

Answer: _____

Justify your answer.

_____

_____

✂ -

Parent Activities

1. Ask your child to design an animal or robot made of different geometric shapes. Classify the shapes based on the sides and angles. For example, "This shape is a rectangle because it has 4 right angles and 2 pairs of parallel sides."

2. Play "I Spy" with geometry terms. Look for objects that contain geometric attributes, and describe them for your child to find. For example, "I spy an object that has an acute angle." "I spy something that has perpendicular lines."

1 Logan ate 3 slices of a large quesadilla that was cut into equal slices. The section Logan ate formed a 108° angle from the center of the circle. What was the measure of the angle formed by each slice?

Answer: _____

Into how many slices was Logan's original quesadilla cut?

Answer: _____

Explain how you found your answers.

_____

_____

_____

_____

2 Theo received a large chocolate chip cookie cake shaped like a circle. He decided to freeze the cookie to make it last longer. Every day, he ate one section of the cookie. Each section formed a 9° angle with a vertex at the center of the cookie. How many days did it take Theo to eat $\frac{1}{4}$ of the cookie?

Answer: _____

How many days did it take Theo to eat the whole cookie?

Answer: _____

Explain how you found your answers.

_____

_____

_____

Journal

How are degrees on a thermometer and degrees of an angle similar and different?

_____

_____

_____

Vocabulary Activity

Complete the steps using the circle. Then answer the questions below.

- Label the center of the circle as point *O*.
- Label the points shown on the circle, in order, as points *A*, *B*, *C*, *D*, *E*, *F*, *G*, and *H*.
- Draw line segments from the center of the circle to each labeled point to form 8 angles. The center of the circle is the vertex of each angle.

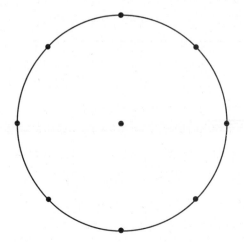

How many one-degree angles compose the whole circle?

Answer: _____

What is the measure of ∠*AOB*?

Answer: _____

Name an angle that measures 180°.

Answer: _____

motivation**math**™LEVEL 4

Standards 4.7(C) – Readiness, 4.7(D) – Supporting

Imagine that you and your friends have decided to form a new club. You are in charge of designing the clubhouse. Draw a floor plan for the clubhouse that includes angles of 90°, 180°, 45°, and 30°. Use a protractor to sketch the angles.

Journal

Analysis
i
Analyze

Many different occupations involve the use and measure of angles. Some examples include architects, surveyors, carpenters, drafters, engineers, cartographers, and pilots. Select one of these occupations and explain how angles and angle measures are an important part of the profession.

_____

_____

_____

Vocabulary Activity

Draw a picture or write a symbol to represent the meaning of the vocabulary term in each section of the diagram. Then, look for acute angles, obtuse angles, right angles, and straight angles in the diagram.

- Trace acute angles in purple.
- Trace obtuse angles in blue.
- Trace right angles in green.
- Trace straight angles in red.
- Circle the vertices in orange.

	obtuse angle	
right angle	degree / vertex	acute angle
	protractor	
	straight angle	

Compete with a friend to see who can trace and circle more angles and vertices.

1 The diagram shows a square that has been decomposed into 3 triangles.

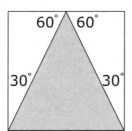

What is the sum of the measures of the 3 angles in the shaded triangle?

Answer: _____

What is the sum of the measures of the 3 angles in each white triangle?

Answer: _____

2 The rectangle and parallelogram are divided into halves.

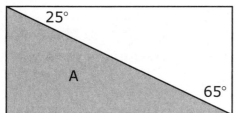

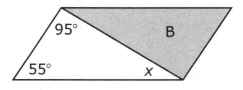

What is the sum of the angles in Triangle A?

Answer: _____

Use a protractor to find the measure of ∠x.

Answer: _____

What is the sum of the angles in Triangle B?

Answer: _____

Explain how you found your answers.

_____

_____

Based on your answers to questions 1 and 2, what generalization can you make about the sum of the measures of the angles in a triangle?

_____

_____

Unit 32 Journal/Vocabulary Activity

Journal

Imagine that you are giving directions to a new student on how to travel from the classroom to the library. Explain how to get to the library using direction words and degree measurements. For example you might write, "First, turn 90° to the left," and so on.

_____

_____

_____

Vocabulary Activity

Follow the directions for the 2 figures below. You will need to use a ruler.

- Draw a ray to decompose the right angle into 2 acute angles.
- Draw a ray to decompose the straight angle into 1 obtuse angle and 1 acute angle.
- With crayons or colored pencils, create an original work of art using your figures.

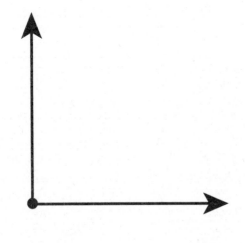

motivation**math**™ LEVEL 4

Motivation Molly says, "It doesn't get much better than this!"

Time for Angles

Play *Time for Angles* with a partner. Each pair of players needs the game board and a paper clip and pencil for the spinner. In turn, each player spins the spinner and locates the clock that shows an angle, *m*, matching the angle measure on the spinner. The player claims the clock by writing his/her name under the clock. If a clock has already been claimed, play passes to the next player. The game ends when all of the clocks have been claimed. The winner is the player who claims more clocks.

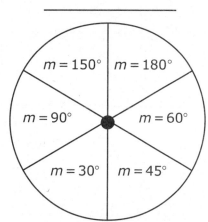

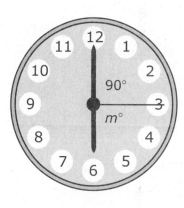

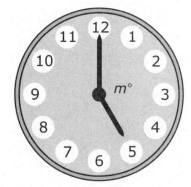

1 Grandmother bought a fan for Maria while she was on vacation. This diagram shows how the fan looked as Maria opened it.

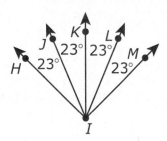

Using the diagram, name 3 angles that each measure 46°.

Answers: _____ , _____ , _____

2 What are the measures of ∠A and ∠B in the square below?

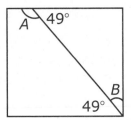

Answers: ∠A = _____, ∠B = _____

Explain how you found your answers.

_____

_____

3 Angle *HGK* measures 132°. What is the measure of angle *JGH*?

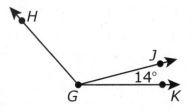

Answer: _____

4 A tangram is a square puzzle with seven pieces. The pieces include a small square, a parallelogram, two large triangles, one medium triangle, and two small triangles as shown in this tangram diagram.

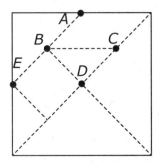

If ∠*DBC* and ∠*CBA* have equal measures, what is the measure of one of these angles?

Answer: _____

Explain how you found your answer.

_____

_____

_____

Parent Activities

1. Conduct a family scavenger hunt for angles found in nature. Have your child sketch the angles and then measure them with a protractor.

2. Place a yardstick or ruler across the opening of a door. Have your child estimate the size of angles by opening and adjusting the door to approximate given measures (e.g., Position the door to show an angle of 90°, 45°, etc.).

Use the table to answer questions 1–3.

This conversion table shows equivalent measures of weight in the customary system of measurement.

Number of Pounds	Number of Ounces
1	16
2	32
3	48

1 Caroline's baby brother weighed 7 pounds when he was born. How many ounces did Caroline's baby brother weigh? Show all work.

Answer: _____

2 Mrs. Neal's candy recipe uses 8 ounces of chocolate chips. Will Mrs. Neal use more or less than 1 pound of chocolate chips?

Answer: _____

Explain your answer.

_____

_____

3 Lamont tracks the growth of his pet hamster. Should Lamont report the hamster's weight in pounds or ounces?

Answer: _____

Explain your answer.

_____

_____

Use the table to answer questions 4 and 5.

This conversion table shows equivalent measures of length in the metric system of measurement.

Number of Millimeters	Number of Centimeters	Number of Meters
1,000	100	1
2,000	200	2
	300	
5,000		5
	700	
		10

4 Complete the conversion table above by supplying the missing numbers.

5 Edgar's bedroom closet has a length of 4 meters. How many centimeters long is Edgar's closet? Show all work.

Answer: _____

6 Place a ✓ before items below that are best measured in millimeters. Place a ★ before items that are best measured in centimeters. Place an **X** before items that are best measured in meters.

_____ the length of a flea

_____ the width of your math book

_____ the height of a candle

_____ the width of a point (•)

_____ the distance to the school library

Use the table to answer questions 1–3.

This conversion table shows equivalent measures of capacity in the customary system of measurement.

Number of Cups	Number of Pints	Number of Quarts	Number of Gallons
4	2	1	$\frac{1}{4}$
8	4	2	$\frac{1}{2}$
16	8	4	1

1 Which of these rows can be added to the table to show the equivalent measures for a capacity of 2 gallons?

Ⓐ
24	12	6	2

Ⓑ
32	18	9	2

Ⓒ
32	16	8	2

Ⓓ
36	18	9	2

2 Mrs. Winston makes fruit punch from a recipe that requires 3 quarts of ginger ale. How many pints of ginger ale does Mrs. Winston need?

Ⓕ 6 pt   Ⓗ 10 pt

Ⓖ 7 pt   Ⓙ 12 pt

3 Coach Olson fills a cooler with 40 pints of water for his baseball team. Which procedure can be used to find the number of quarts equivalent to 40 pints?

Ⓐ Number of pints × 2 = number of quarts

Ⓑ Number of pints × 4 = number of quarts

Ⓒ Number of pints ÷ 2 = number of quarts

Ⓓ Number of pints ÷ 8 = number of quarts

Use the table to answer questions 4–6.

This conversion table shows equivalent measures of mass in the metric system of measurement.

Number of Kilograms	Number of Grams
1	1,000
2	2,000
4	4,000

4 What is the relationship between the number of kilograms and the number of grams?

Ⓕ The number of grams is $\frac{1}{10}$ the number of kilograms.

Ⓖ The number of kilograms is 100 times the number of grams.

Ⓗ The number of kilograms is $\frac{1}{2}$ the number of grams.

Ⓙ The number of grams is 1,000 times the number of kilograms.

5 A female tiger at the Ft. Worth Zoo has a mass of 84 kilograms. What is the mass, in grams, of the tiger?

Ⓐ 840,000 g   Ⓒ 8,400 g

Ⓑ 84,000 g   Ⓓ 840 g

6 Which of the following would most likely have a mass of 1 gram?

Ⓕ A box of marbles

Ⓖ A large dog

Ⓗ A paper clip

Ⓙ A can of soup

Use the table to answer questions 1 and 2.

Arvin made a conversion table to show equivalent measures of capacity in the metric system of measurement.

Number of Liters	Number of Milliliters
1	1,000
2	2,000
3	3,000
4	4,000

1 Arvin buys a fish tank that holds 100 liters of water. What is the capacity, in milliliters, of the fish tank?

Ⓐ 1,000 mL

Ⓑ 10,000 mL

Ⓒ 100,000 mL

Ⓓ 0.01 mL

2 Arvin read that an elephant drinks between 100,000 and 300,000 milliliters of water per day. How many liters is this?

Ⓕ Between 1,000 and 3,000 liters

Ⓖ Between 100 and 300 liters

Ⓗ Between 10 and 30 liters

Ⓙ Between 1 and 3 liters

3 Which of the following has a capacity of about 1 liter?

Ⓐ A medicine dropper

Ⓑ A swimming pool

Ⓒ A bottle of water

Ⓓ A bathtub

Use the table to answer questions 4 and 5.

Rochelle made this conversion table to show equivalent measures of length in the customary system of measurement.

Number of Yards	Number of Feet	Number of Inches
2	6	72
4	12	144
6	18	216

4 Which of these could be a row in Rochelle's table?

Ⓕ

8	24	264

Ⓖ

9	18	180

Ⓗ

12	48	576

Ⓙ

10	30	360

5 Rochelle and her father watched a football game on Monday night. The quarterback threw the ball a total of 318 yards. How many feet did the quarterback throw the ball?

Record your answer and fill in the bubbles on the grid below. Be sure to use the correct place value.

⊘	⊘	⊘	⊘	•	⊘	⊘
⓪	⓪	⓪	⓪		⓪	⓪
①	①	①	①		①	①
②	②	②	②		②	②
③	③	③	③		③	③
④	④	④	④		④	④
⑤	⑤	⑤	⑤		⑤	⑤
⑥	⑥	⑥	⑥		⑥	⑥
⑦	⑦	⑦	⑦		⑦	⑦
⑧	⑧	⑧	⑧		⑧	⑧
⑨	⑨	⑨	⑨		⑨	⑨

Use the table to answer questions 1–3.

Cedrick made this conversion table to show equivalent measures of weight in the customary system of measurement.

Number of Pounds	1	2	5	10
Number of Ounces	16	32	80	160

1 Cedrick weighs 69 pounds. How can he use the table to convert his weight to ounces?

Ⓐ He can divide 69 by 16.

Ⓑ He can multiply 69 × 16.

Ⓒ He can divide 69 by 16.

Ⓓ He can add 69 and 16.

2 Cedrick's mother sends him to the store to buy apples for an apple pie. Her recipe calls for 3 pounds of apples. How many ounces of apples should Cedrick buy?

Ⓕ 48 oz   Ⓗ 38 oz

Ⓖ 35 oz   Ⓙ 19 oz

3 Cedrick's school recycles aluminum cans. Last month the school recycled 39 pounds of cans. How many ounces did the school recycle?

Record your answer and fill in the bubbles on the grid below. Be sure to use the correct place value.

				•		
⓪	⓪	⓪	⓪		⓪	⓪
①	①	①	①		①	①
②	②	②	②		②	②
③	③	③	③		③	③
④	④	④	④		④	④
⑤	⑤	⑤	⑤		⑤	⑤
⑥	⑥	⑥	⑥		⑥	⑥
⑦	⑦	⑦	⑦		⑦	⑦
⑧	⑧	⑧	⑧		⑧	⑧
⑨	⑨	⑨	⑨		⑨	⑨

4 Allison created this table to show the relationship between metric measurements of length.

Meters	1	2	4
Centimeters	100	200	400

Allison wants to extend the table to show equivalent measures for 6, 10, and 25 meters. Which of the following shows the correct conversions for these lengths?

Ⓕ
6	10	25
60	100	250

Ⓖ
6	10	25
6,000	10,000	250,000

Ⓗ
6	10	25
600	1,000	25,000

Ⓙ
6	10	25
600	1,000	2,500

5 Which of the following shows the relative sizes of one centimeter and one meter?

Ⓐ The width of a fingernail and the distance from a doorknob to the floor

Ⓑ The length of a new crayon and the length of an unsharpened pencil

Ⓒ The height of a baby and the height of an adult

Ⓓ The length of a little finger and the length of a football field

1 The bar graph below shows the average weights of four different species of dinosaur.

Dinosaur Weights

Name of Dinosaur:
- Triceratops
- Parasaurolophus
- Tyrannosaurus Rex
- Stegosaurus

Weight (tons): 0 2 4 6 8 10

What is the difference, in pounds, between the weight of a triceratops and the weight of a stegosaurus?

Explain how you found your answer.

_____

_____

Answer: _____   _____

2 The Eastlake City Council is planning a Founder's Day reception. Fifty gallons of punch are needed to serve the 800 people who are expected to attend. The mayor's wife has a recipe that makes punch for 100 people. She said, "I have revised my recipe to make enough punch for 800 people." The revised recipe requires the following ingredients:

- 32 quarts pineapple juice
- 48 pints orange juice
- 16 cups lemon juice
- 14 half-gallon containers of orange or lime sherbet
- Enough ginger ale to total 50 gallons

How many gallons of ginger ale will be needed for the punch recipe?

Answer: _____

Journal

In the Laura Ingalls Wilder book, *Little House on the Prairie*, Pa's nickname for Laura is "Half-pint." What is a half-pint? Why do you think Pa called Laura by this name?

_____

_____

Vocabulary Activity

In the metric system of measurement, prefixes are combined with the base unit of measure to identify relative sizes of measurement. Some of the more commonly used prefixes are shown in the table below along with the base units for length, capacity, and mass.

Prefix	Meaning	Length	Capacity	Mass
milli-	$\frac{1}{1000}$ (base unit ÷ 1,000)	millimeter	milliliter	milligram
centi-	$\frac{1}{100}$ (base unit ÷ 100)	centimeter	centiliter	centigram
(base unit)		meter	liter	gram
kilo-	1,000 (base unit × 1,000)	kilometer	kiloliter	kilogram

Use the information on the table to explain the meaning of the measurement words given. The first word has been completed as an example.

millimeter — <u>one-thousandth the length of a meter; 1,000 millimeters = 1 meter</u>

milliliter — _____

milligram — _____

centimeter — _____

kilometer — _____

kilogram — _____

Motivation Mike says, "Bravo! You're a math champ!"

Conversion Crossword

Use the clues to complete the *Conversion Crossword* puzzle.

Across

3. 1,760 of these = 1 mile
4. $\frac{1}{10}$ the value of a dime
7. 1,000 milliliters
8. $\frac{1}{2}$ pint
9. 16 of these = 1 pound
11. 1,000 milligrams
13. 1,000 of these = 1 liter
14. $\frac{1}{8}$ cup
16. 100 centimeters
18. 100 of these = 1 meter
21. 4 cups or 2 pints
23. 16 ounces
24. 60 minutes
25. $\frac{1}{3}$ yard

Down

1. 8 pints or 4 quarts
2. 1,000 meters
4. $\frac{1}{8}$ gallon
5. 5 pennies
6. 1,000 grams
10. $\frac{1}{10}$ the value of a dollar
12. 1,000 of these = 1 gram
13. 60 seconds
15. 10 dimes
17. 60 of these = 1 minute
19. 2,000 pounds
20. 5,280 feet
21. $\frac{1}{4}$ the value of a dollar
22. $\frac{1}{12}$ of a foot

Name _____

Use the table to answer questions 1 and 2.

Adrian begins a conversion table to show the relationship between metric units of mass.

Number of Kilograms	Number of Grams
1	1,000
2	2,000
	3,000
4	
	15,000
21	

1 Complete Adrian's table by writing the missing numbers in the boxes.

2 Explain the relationship between the number of kilograms and the number of grams.

_____

_____

_____

Use the table to answer questions 3–5.

Ella made this conversion table to show customary units of length.

Number of Inches	Number of Feet	Number of Yards
12	1	$\frac{1}{3}$
24	2	$\frac{2}{3}$
36	3	1
72		2
		3
		4

3 Complete Ella's conversion table by writing the missing numbers in the boxes.

4 Ella makes hair bows from colored ribbon. She has 78 feet of ribbon. How many inches of ribbon does Ella have? Show all work.

Answer: _____

5 How many yards of ribbon does Ella have?

Answer: _____

✂ -

Parent Activities

1. Have your child estimate how many cups of milk your family needs for one week and convert the amount to quarts and/or gallons. Let your child determine how much milk to buy at the grocery store.

2. Use a marker to divide a yardstick into 3 feet. Have your child use the yardstick to measure lengths of household items and express each measure in yards, feet, or inches. Then have your child multiply or divide to convert the measures to other units.

3. Gather a variety of plastic containers labeled with units of customary capacity (e.g., milk or juice containers, ice cream, yogurt, sour cream cartons). Discuss the capacity relationship between the containers. Verify by pouring water from one container to another.

1 Mr. Mathis has a piece of wood that is 8 feet long. He uses 58 inches of the wood to make a shelf. How many inches of wood does Mr. Mathis have left?

38

Answer: _____

2 Anton buys 3 bottles that each contain $\frac{1}{2}$ liter of juice. Over a three-day weekend, Anton drinks 400 milliliters of juice each day. After the three-day weekend, how many milliliters of juice does Anton have left? Show all work.

Answer: _____

3 Justin arrives home from baseball practice at 6:00 P.M. He spends 30 minutes eating dinner, 50 minutes completing his homework, an hour and fifteen minutes watching TV, and a quarter hour taking a shower and brushing his teeth. When he completes all these activities, Justin goes to bed. What time does Justin go to bed? Use the number line below to help solve the problem.

6:00 6:30 7:00 7:30 8:00 8:30 9:00

Answer: 8:50 Pm

4 Maria, a bike mechanic, charges $60 per hour of labor. She works on a racing bike for 2 hours 20 minutes, a cruiser bike for 1 hour, and a child's bike for 40 minutes. What is the total amount Maria charges for labor? Show all work.

Answer: $240.00

5 A quarter has a mass of about 6 grams. The quarters in Riley's coin collection have a total mass of 3 kilograms. How many quarters are in Riley's collection? Show all work.

Answer: 500 quarts

6 Last week, Camille walked on the treadmill for $13\frac{1}{4}$ hours. She spent the same amount of time on the treadmill each day except Sunday. On Sunday, she spent $1\frac{1}{4}$ hours walking on the treadmill. How many minutes did Camille walk on the treadmill on Monday? Show all work.

Answer: _____

1 Each student in Mrs. Sands' class jumps rope for 6 minutes. The students jump a combined total of 2 hours. How many students are in Mrs. Sands' class?

Ⓐ 30

Ⓑ 12

Ⓒ 24

Ⓓ 20

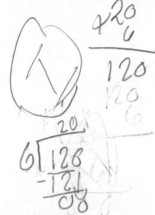

2 A standard bathtub holds 40 gallons of water. Which shows the number of pints and the number of quarts equivalent to 40 gallons?

Ⓕ 160 pt and 320 qt

Ⓖ 320 pt and 160 qt

Ⓗ 5 pt and 10 qt

Ⓙ 240 pt and 120 qt

3 Mrs. Goff's family loves salsa. She purchases a box that contains 6 jars of salsa. The total mass of the 6 jars is 9 kilograms. What is the mass, in grams, of each jar of salsa?

Ⓐ 15 g

Ⓑ 54 g

Ⓒ 660 g

Ⓓ 1,500 g

4 Jaclyn planned a girls' sleepover. She purchased two 2-liter bottles of soda and 6 bottles of water that each hold $\frac{1}{2}$ liter. Her mother made 2 liters of fruit punch. How many milliliters of drinks did Jaclyn have for her party?

Ⓕ 10,000 mL

Ⓖ 9,000 mL

Ⓗ 900 mL

Ⓙ 10.5 mL

5 Jennell has a piece of ribbon that measures 2 yards 8 inches in length. She cuts the ribbon into 4 equal pieces. What is the length, in inches, of each piece of ribbon?

Ⓐ 20 in.   Ⓒ 72 in.

Ⓑ 80 in.   Ⓓ 24 in.

6 Kylie went to the store and bought two packages of cookies, three candy bars, and six fruit drinks. The table shows the cost of each item.

Kylie's Purchases

Item	Cost
Cookies	$3.50
Candy bar	$0.75
Fruit drink	$1.00

If Kylie paid with a $20 bill, how much change did she receive?

Ⓕ $4.75   Ⓗ $7.00

Ⓖ $5.25   Ⓙ $15.25

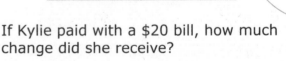

1 Mrs. Delaney needs to move 396 books from her classroom to the library. Each book weighs $\frac{1}{2}$ pound. She divides the books into 6 equal stacks. What will be the weight, in ounces, of each stack?

Ⓐ 198 oz

© 66 oz

Ⓑ 528 oz

Ⓓ 33 oz

2 Dennis prepared for a piano concert. He practiced for 1 hour 30 minutes on Monday, 2 hours 45 minutes on Tuesday, and $3\frac{1}{4}$ hours on Wednesday. How many total minutes did Dennis practice on these three days?

Ⓕ $7\frac{1}{2}$ minutes

Ⓖ 180 minutes

Ⓗ 255 minutes

Ⓙ 450 minutes

3 The Grand Hotel wants to place a carpet runner at the entrance to welcome special guests. The distance from the curb to the door of the hotel is $12\frac{3}{4}$ yards. The distance from the door to the welcome counter is an additional $15\frac{1}{4}$ yards. If the hotel places a carpet runner from the curb to the welcome counter, what will be the length, in feet, of the carpet runner?

Ⓐ 28 ft

© 84 ft

Ⓑ 42 ft

Ⓓ 336 ft

4 At Super Mart, a pound of grapes costs $1.80. Ariana purchased $1\frac{1}{2}$ pounds of grapes. Ariana gave the clerk a ten-dollar bill. How much change did Ariana receive?

Ⓕ $7.30

Ⓖ $8.20

Ⓗ $9.10

Ⓙ $6.70

5 Adam's mother bought 5 liters of apple juice to serve at his party. Adam and his five guests each drank 675 milliliters of juice. How many milliliters of juice were left?

Ⓐ 1,000 mL

Ⓑ 4,050 mL

© 950 mL

Ⓓ 1,575 mL

6 Rex purchased 2 kilograms of beef, 4 kilograms of chicken, and 3 kilograms of ribs for a barbeque. How many grams of meat did Rex purchase?

Ⓕ 9.5 g

Ⓖ 6,000 g

Ⓗ 7,500 g

Ⓙ 9,000 g

Unit 34 Assessment

1 Mary, Shalinda, and Ray had $135 to spend on a community garden. They spent $54.85 on fertilizer. Then they spent $24.50 on bedding plants and $46.00 on roses. How much money did the children have left?

Ⓐ $125.35

Ⓑ $10.65

Ⓒ $9.65

Ⓓ $260.35

2 Clay wants to make banners for his school. He needs 1 yard of blue fabric, $\frac{3}{4}$ yard of red fabric, and $\frac{1}{4}$ yard of white fabric for each banner. How many inches of fabric will Clay use to make 8 banners?

Ⓕ 2 in. Ⓗ 192 in.

Ⓖ 72 in. Ⓙ 576 in.

3 Mrs. Patton's baby weighs 10 pounds 2 ounces. Mrs. Mishima's baby weighs 7 pounds 9 ounces. How many more ounces does Mrs. Patton's baby weigh than Mrs. Mishima's baby?

Ⓐ 48 oz

Ⓑ 41 oz

Ⓒ 23 oz

Ⓓ 16 oz

4 Hayley gets up at 6:25 A.M. She leaves her house at 7:19 A.M. to catch the bus for school. How many minutes does Hayley have to get ready before she leaves for school?

Ⓕ 64 minutes

Ⓖ 49 minutes

Ⓗ 59 minutes

Ⓙ 54 minutes

5 Lavar purchased drinks for a school party. He bought 5 gallons of juice, 4 gallons of water, 3 gallons of punch, and 1 gallon of tea. How many pints of liquid did Lavar purchase?

Ⓐ 13 pt

Ⓑ 26 pt

Ⓒ 52 pt

Ⓓ 104 pt

6 Sally has a spool that holds 5 meters of ribbon. She uses 2 meters of ribbon on a wreath and $\frac{1}{2}$ meter of ribbon to wrap a gift. Sally also cuts off 25 centimeters to use as a bookmark and 78 centimeters to use as a hair ribbon. How many centimeters of ribbon are left on the spool?

Ⓕ 110 cm

Ⓖ 147 cm

Ⓗ 353 cm

Ⓙ 500 cm

 motivation**math**™ LEVEL 4

1 Baby Zoe drinks 4 fluid ounces of milk 6 times each day. How much milk should her mother buy to have enough milk for one week? Show your work.

Answer: _____

Zoe's mother wants to buy milk in containers of the same size. Should she buy pints, quarts, or gallons in order to have the least amount of leftover milk?

Answer: _____

Explain your thinking.

_____

_____

_____

Is there a combination of gallon, quart, and pint containers that will give Zoe's mother exactly the right amount of milk for Zoe? Explain your answer.

Answer: _____

_____

2 Grady organizes a basketball tournament at his school. Five games will be played in the school gym over a 3-hour time period. There will be a 15-minute break between games. How many minutes will each game last? Use words, numbers, or pictures to help solve the problem.

Answer: _____

Journal

What unit would be best for measuring sand? The distance from Earth to Mars? The weight of a cell phone? The length of a soccer field? Do any of these questions have more than one possible answer? Explain why or why not.

_____

_____

_____

_____

Vocabulary Activity

Sort each vocabulary word in the word box into the proper category below.

Word Box			
centimeter	gram	mile	pint
cup	hour	milliliter	pound
dime	inch	millimeter	quart
dollar	kilogram	minute	quarter
fluid ounce	kilometer	nickel	second
foot/feet	liter	ounce	ton
gallon	meter	penny	yard

Time	Money	Length	Capacity	Weight/Mass

   motivation**math**™LEVEL 4 ©2014 mentoring**minds**.com

Motivation Molly says, "Fantastic work!"

Connect Four, Measure More

Play *Connect Four, Measure More* with a partner. Each pair needs one game sheet and a pencil and paper clip to use with the spinner. Each player needs a different color crayon or marker. In turn, each player spins the spinner to identify a category of measure. The player selects an abbreviation from the game board representing a unit of measure for the category spun. For example, if a player spins *weight/mass*, he/she may select one of the following: oz, lb, T, g, or kg. The player shades the square with his/her color.
The first player to connect four squares in a row wins the game.

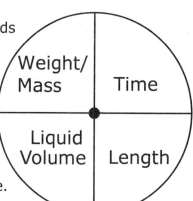

min	oz	ft	qt	yr	g	c	in.
yd	L	day	gal	ft	km	h	m
kg	mL	mm	s	m	T	mL	lb
s	in.	wk	qt	min	fl oz	cm	mL
m	yd	mL	pt	km	in.	h	mm
mi	lb	qt	L	ft	min	wk	L
pt	km	g	h	gal	oz	qt	s
day	fl oz	cm	kg	cup	T	yr	mi

Customary Measures

c — cup	in. — inch	qt — quart
day — day	lb — pound	s — second
fl oz — fluid ounce	mi — mile	T — ton
ft — foot	min — minute	wk — week
gal — gallon	oz — ounce	yd — yard
h — hour	pt — pint	yr — year

Metric Measures

cm — centimeter	mm — millimeter
g — gram	L — liter
kg — kilogram	m — meter
km — kilometer	mL — milliliter

Unit 34 Homework

1 Binta sets the table for a dinner party. She arranges five 12-inch-long placemats along one side of the table. She leaves 2 inches between the placemats and at each end of the table. What is the length of Binta's table in feet? Draw a picture and show your work.

Write an equation that could be used to solve the problem.

Answer: _____

2 Mitch collects Presidential dollar coins. Each coin weighs 8 grams. Mitch's coin collection weighs a total of 2 kilograms. How many dollar coins are in Mitch's collection? Show all work.

Answer: _____

3 Kira and Ivan are organizing a water balloon game. Kira has two 5-gallon buckets filled with water. Ivan has three 3-gallon buckets filled with water. How many quarts of water do the two children have? Show all work.

Answer: _____

4 Jevon arrives home from school at 3:10 P.M. It takes him 15 minutes to eat a snack, $\frac{1}{2}$ hour to complete his homework, 7 minutes to change clothes and pack his gear for soccer practice, and 18 minutes to ride his bicycle to the soccer field. Use the number line to help solve the problem.

3:00 3:15 3:30 3:45 4:00 4:15 4:30

At what time does Jevon arrive at soccer practice?

Answer: _____

✂ -

Parent Activities

1. Help your child with conversions of measurements from larger units to smaller units and smaller units to larger units by having him/her measure water using different sizes of measuring cups.

2. Use an analog clock (not a digital clock) to help your child understand intervals of time and how time elapses. Create scenarios for your child to "act out" times with the clock (e.g., "You need to arrive at school at 7:30. It takes 12 minutes to get to school. What time should you leave the house?").

 motivation**math**™ LEVEL 4

1 A stem-and-leaf plot is used to display Data Set A and Data Set B below. Study each data set. Then fill in the missing numbers in the key for each stem-and-leaf plot.

Data Set A: 29, 30, 29, 30, 29, 29, 41

Data Set B: 299, 304, 293, 300, 298, 298, 412

Data Set A

Stem	Leaves
2	9 9 9 9
3	0 0
4	1

__ | __ represents _____

Data Set B

Stem	Leaves
29	3 8 8 9
30	0 4
41	2

__ | __ represents _____

Explain your answer for Data Set B.

_____

_____

2 Fill in the blanks to create Data Set C. Display your data set as a stem-and-leaf plot. Your data set and stem-and-leaf plot must match the key below.

Data Set C: _____, _____, _____, _____, _____, _____, _____

Data Set C

Stem	Leaves

502 | 7   represents 5,027

Unit 35 Journal/Vocabulary Activity

Journal

How is a dot plot like a bar graph?

_____

_____

How is a dot plot different from a bar graph?

_____

_____

Vocabulary Activity

Write *frequency table*, *dot plot*, or *stem-and-leaf plot* on the line below each data display. Then answer the questions.

Colors of Strings

Color	Frequency
Red	1
Blue	3
Black	5
Gray	2
White	2

Lengths of Strings

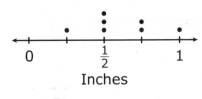

Inches

Lengths of Strings (ft)

Stem	Leaves
1	2 3
2	0 0 5
3	4 6
4	2 2

1 | 2   represents 12

_____   _____   _____

How many categories are used in the frequency table?

Answer: _____

What is the data set for the dot plot?

Answer: _____

What is the data set for the stem-and-leaf plot?

Answer: _____

   motivation**math**™LEVEL 4   ©2014 mentoring**minds**.com

Motivation Mike says, "Keep up the good work!"

Measurement Mission

Go on a *Measurement Mission* with a group. Each group needs an inch ruler and 1 activity sheet. Find 6–8 objects that are between 2 and 6 inches long. Measure the objects to the nearest half inch, and record the data on this table. Use the data to create a dot plot. Then join another group, and work together to create a frequency table that displays the combined data from both dot plots.

Lengths of Objects

Object								
Length (in.)								

Lengths of Objects

Inches

Lengths of Objects Measured by Both Groups

Length (in.)	Frequency

Unit 35 Homework

1 A group of students weighed rocks during science class. The students recorded the data on this chart.

Weights of Rocks (pounds)		
Rock A - $\frac{4}{8}$	Rock B - $\frac{7}{8}$	Rock C - $\frac{3}{8}$
Rock D - $\frac{5}{8}$	Rock E - $\frac{3}{8}$	Rock F - $\frac{7}{8}$
Rock G - $\frac{2}{8}$	Rock H - $\frac{6}{8}$	Rock I - $\frac{3}{8}$
Rock J - $\frac{5}{8}$	Rock K - $\frac{3}{8}$	Rock L - $\frac{5}{8}$

Use the data from the chart to complete the dot plot below. Be sure to include a title above and a unit of measurement below your dot plot.

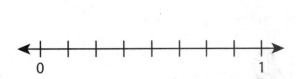

0   1

2 Jeremy used this frequency table to show the heights of his friends. Complete the stem-and-leaf plot below to show the heights of Jeremy's friends.

Heights of Friends

Height (in.)	56	58	60	62	64
Frequency	1	2	3	1	4

Heights of Friends (in.)

Stem	Leaves
5	
6	

5 | 6   represents 56

3 Gilbert received these grades in social studies class. Create a stem-and-leaf plot to display Gilbert's grades. Be sure to include a title and key.

78, 99, 68, 74, 82, 80,

90, 95, 83, 85, 78, 100

Stem	Leaves
6	
7	
8	
9	
10	

| represents

✂ -

Parent Activities

1. Sort a set of coins by dates, and use a frequency table to display the data.

2. Use a family tree to discover the number of letters in each family member's first name. Create a dot plot to display the data. Discuss math questions that can be answered with the dot plot.

3. Work with your child to create a stem-and-leaf plot to display grades from graded assignments.

Use the dot plot to answer questions 1–3.

Lisa joined a summer book club. She recorded the number of hours she read each day for 12 days. Lisa displayed the data on a dot plot.

Lisa's Reading Times

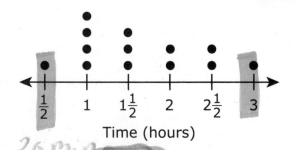

Time (hours)

1 What is the difference between the longest amount of time Lisa read in one day and the shortest amount of time she read in one day? Show all work.

36 min

longest= 3 hours
shortest= 1/2 hours

Answer: _____*2 1/2 hours*_____

2 How many days did Lisa read for fewer than 2 hours?

Answer: _____*8 days*_____

3 What was Lisa's combined reading time for the 3 days on which she read the most hours? Show all work.

3 hours
2 hour
hours

Answer: _____*8 hours*_____

Use the frequency table to answer questions 4 and 5.

Jordan threw a Frisbee® several times and measured each distance to the nearest 0.25 meter. He used this frequency table to show the measurements.

Jordan's Throws

Distance (m)	10.75	11	11.25	11.5
Frequency	2	5	2	1

4 What is the combined distance of Jordan's 2 shortest throws?

Answer: _____*21.50*_____

5 What is the combined distance of Jordan's 3 longest throws?

Answer: _____*34.60*_____

6 Cade used the stem-and-leaf plot below to record the numbers of dollars he paid for different video games.

Dollars Paid for Games

Stem	Leaves
1	4 8 9
2	3 8 8 8
3	2 4 5 5 7

1 | 4   represents 14

14,18,19
23, 28, 28
28, 32,34
35,35,37

What was the total cost of all the games with purchase prices between $20 and $30?

Answer: _____*$107.00*_____

Unit 36 Guided Practice

1 An amusement park worker takes a daily survey to find the favorite rides of park guests. This frequency table displays the worker's data for one day.

Favorite Rides

Ride	Frequency
Race Cars	709
Spinner	864
Roller Coaster	927
Tilter	652

Which 2 rides have a combined frequency of 1,516?

Ⓐ Race Cars and Spinner

Ⓑ Roller Coaster and Race Cars

Ⓒ Roller Coaster and Tilter

Ⓓ Spinner and Tilter

2 Dan created this stem-and-leaf plot to display the ages, in years, of his 6 uncles.

Ages (years)

Stem	Leaves
2	3
3	8 9 9
4	4
5	9

2 | 3   represents 23

What is the difference between the ages of Dan's two youngest uncles?

Ⓕ 17 years   Ⓗ 16 years

Ⓖ 15 years   Ⓙ Not here

Use the dot plot to answer questions 3–5.

Mrs. Vandiver's class studied coins from different countries. The students measured the diameter of each coin to the nearest $\frac{1}{8}$ inch and recorded the results on this dot plot.

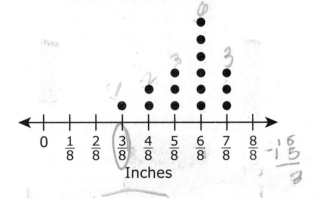

Diameters of Coins

3 What is the difference, in inches, between the coin with the largest diameter and the coin with the smallest diameter?

Ⓐ $\frac{1}{8}$ in.   Ⓒ $\frac{1}{2}$ in.

Ⓑ $\frac{3}{8}$ in.   Ⓓ $\frac{7}{8}$ in.

4 How many coins measured less than $\frac{3}{4}$ inch in diameter?

Ⓕ 6   Ⓗ 1

Ⓖ 0   Ⓙ 12

5 If all the coins with diameters of $\frac{7}{8}$ inch were placed end-to-end, what would be the total length of these coins?

Ⓐ $2\frac{1}{4}$ in.

Ⓑ $2\frac{5}{8}$ in.

Ⓒ 3 in.

Ⓓ $2\frac{7}{8}$ in.

 motivation**math**™ LEVEL 4

Use the frequency table to answer questions 1–3.

George went jogging each day for one week. He recorded his daily distances on this frequency table.

Daily Jogging Distances

Number of Miles	Frequency
0.5	2
1.25	1
1.5	2
2	2

1 What is the combined distance for the days George jogged less than 1.5 miles?

Ⓐ 3 miles

Ⓑ 5.25 miles

Ⓒ 7 miles

Ⓓ 2.25 miles

2 What is the difference between the greatest distance and the least distance George jogged in one day?

Ⓕ 0 miles   Ⓗ 2.5 miles

Ⓖ 1.5 miles   Ⓙ 0.3 mile

3 George decided to jog 1 extra day. On this day, his distance was 2.5 miles. What is George's combined distance for the 3 days in which he jogged 2 or more miles?

Ⓐ 4.5 miles

Ⓑ 4.25 miles

Ⓒ 6.5 miles

Ⓓ 5.5 miles

4 Grace makes this stem-and-leaf plot to show her daily pay for ten days.

Dollars Earned Each Day

Stem	Leaves
1	6 6
2	0 0 4 4 8
3	2 2 6

1 | 6   represents 16

She correctly finds that the answer to a question is $20. Which could be Grace's question?

Ⓕ What is the sum of the two least amounts?

Ⓖ What is the difference of the two greatest amounts?

Ⓗ How many amounts are between $19 and $21?

Ⓙ How much more is the greatest amount than the least amount?

5 This dot plot shows the lengths, rounded to the nearest $\frac{1}{2}$ inch, of the babies born at the hospital last week.

Lengths of Newborn Babies

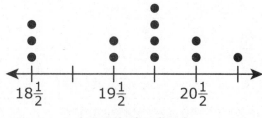

Length (inches)

How many inches longer was the longest baby than the shortest baby?

Ⓐ $2\frac{1}{2}$ in.   Ⓒ $1\frac{1}{2}$ in.

Ⓑ 2 in.   Ⓓ 3 in.

Unit 36 Assessment

Use the dot plot to answer questions 1–3.

A pet store worker weighs each kitten to the nearest 0.05 kilogram. This dot plot shows the weights.

Weights of Kittens

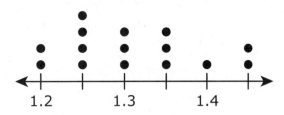

Weight (kilograms)

1 How much more does the heaviest kitten weigh than the lightest kitten?

Ⓐ 0.3 kg

Ⓑ 0.5 kg

Ⓒ 0.25 kg

Ⓓ 2.4 kg

2 All kittens that weigh 1.35 kilograms are placed on a scale together. What weight does the scale display?

Ⓕ 3.95 kg

Ⓖ 3.15 kg

Ⓗ 3 kg

Ⓙ 4.05 kg

3 How many kittens weigh more than 1.25 but less than 1.45 kilograms?

Ⓐ 7

Ⓑ 13

Ⓒ 6

Ⓓ 1

4 Tim measures the heights of the bean plants in his garden to the nearest $\frac{1}{8}$ inch. He displays the data on this frequency table.

Bean Plant Heights

Height (in.)	Frequency
$\frac{5}{8}$	3
$\frac{3}{4}$	2
$\frac{7}{8}$	4
$1\frac{1}{8}$	1

What is the combined height of all bean plants that are $\frac{5}{8}$ inch tall?

Ⓕ $1\frac{5}{8}$ in.   Ⓗ $1\frac{1}{4}$ in.

Ⓖ $1\frac{7}{8}$ in.   Ⓙ 3 in.

5 This stem-and-leaf plot shows the number of multiplication facts each student in a class correctly answered in one minute.

Multiplication Facts

Stem	Leaves
2	7 7 8
3	2 3 4 9
4	0 0 2 5 5
5	1 1 1 5 6

2 | 7   represents 27

What is the difference between the greatest and least numbers of multiplication facts answered correctly?

Ⓐ 29   Ⓒ 28

Ⓑ 31   Ⓓ 24

 motivation**math**™LEVEL 4

1 Kate recorded the lengths of the specimens in her insect collection. She created this dot plot of the data.

Insect Lengths

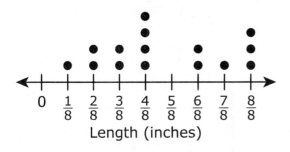

Length (inches)

Kate forgot to record the length of one insect, but she knows that the total length of all the insects is 9 inches.

How many eighths are equivalent to 9?

Answer: _____

What is the length of the insect Kate forgot to record?

Answer: _____

Explain how you found your answer.

_____

_____

_____

_____

2 The frequency table shows the numbers of students who earned different grades on a math test. Create a stem-and-leaf plot that could represent the data on the frequency table. Write a question about the data on your stem-and-leaf plot. Trade with a friend and answer each other's questions.

Math Test Grades

Grade	Frequency
66–70	2
71–75	2
76–80	3
81–85	4
86–90	1
91–95	2
96–100	2

Math Test Grades

Stem | Leaves

| represents

Question
Answer

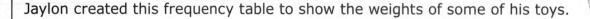

Journal

Jaylon created this frequency table to show the weights of some of his toys.

Weights of Toys

Weight (oz)	4	$4\frac{1}{2}$	$5\frac{1}{2}$	$6\frac{1}{4}$	$6\frac{3}{4}$
Frequency	7	10	5	3	2

Jaylon wants to display the data in a different form. Which should he use? Circle one.

Dot Plot   Stem-and-Leaf Plot

Explain your answer. _____

_____

Vocabulary Activity

Each data display represents a different group of plants. Study the data and complete each sentence below with *frequency table*, *stem-and-leaf plot*, or *dot plot*.

Plant Heights

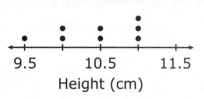

Height (cm)

Plant Heights (mm)

Stem	Leaves
6	1 6
7	4 4 9
8	0 0 8 8

6 | 1   represents 61

Plant Heights

Height (in.)	Frequency
$4\frac{1}{2}$	2
5	7
$5\frac{1}{2}$	1
6	3

If the difference between the greatest frequency
and the least frequency equals 6, the data display is a _____.

If the sum of the heights of the
3 tallest plants equals 33, the data display is a _____.

If the difference between the heights of
the 2 shortest plants equals 5, the data display is a _____.

Motivation Molly says, "Aren't you the clever one!"

The Plot Thickens!

Play *The Plot Thickens!* with a partner. Each pair needs a game board, a two-color counter, and two game tokens. In turn, players toss the counter and move 1 space for red and 2 spaces for the other color. The player reads the statement in the space and identifies which plot makes the statement true. If the player correctly states that both plots make the statement true, the player doubles the point value. Players record tally marks on the frequency table to show the number of points earned. If a player incorrectly answers the question, no points are earned for that turn. When one player reaches STOP, players count and total the tally marks. The player with more total points wins.

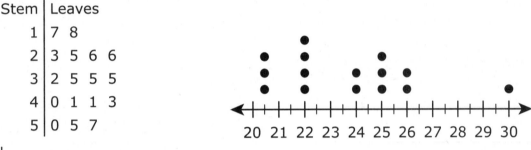

Stem	Leaves
1	7 8
2	3 5 6 6
3	2 5 5 5
4	0 1 1 3
5	0 5 7

1 | 7   represents 17

20 21 22 23 24 25 26 27 28 29 30
Inches

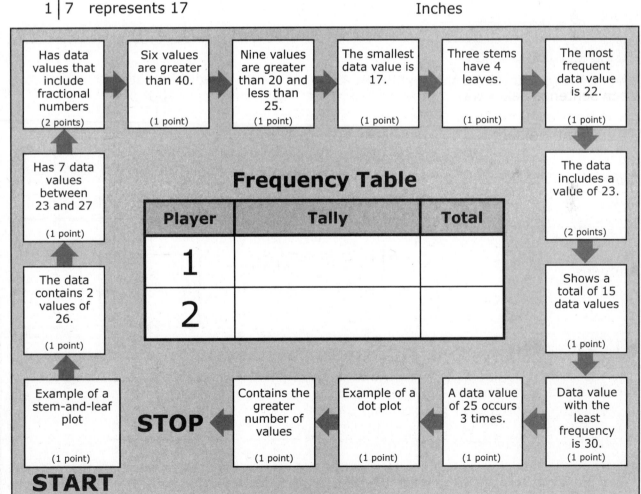

| Has data values that include fractional numbers (2 points) | Six values are greater than 40. (1 point) | Nine values are greater than 20 and less than 25. (1 point) | The smallest data value is 17. (1 point) | Three stems have 4 leaves. (1 point) | The most frequent data value is 22. (1 point) |

| Has 7 data values between 23 and 27 (1 point) | | **Frequency Table** | | | The data includes a value of 23. (2 points) |

Frequency Table

Player	Tally	Total
1		
2		

| The data contains 2 values of 26. (1 point) | | | | | Shows a total of 15 data values (1 point) |

| Example of a stem-and-leaf plot (1 point) | **STOP** | Contains the greater number of values (1 point) | Example of a dot plot (1 point) | A data value of 25 occurs 3 times. (1 point) | Data value with the least frequency is 30. (1 point) |

START

Use the dot plot to answer questions 1–3.

Terrell measured the lengths of the crayons in a box. He displayed the results on a dot plot.

Crayon Lengths

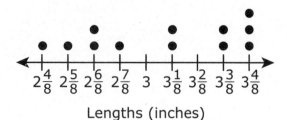

Lengths (inches)

1 If the three longest crayons are placed end to end, what is the total length?

Answer: _____

2 How many inches longer is one of the longest crayons than the shortest crayon?

Answer: _____

3 How many crayons are less than 3 inches long?

Answer: _____

4 A group of students participated in a jump rope contest. This frequency table shows each student's jumping time.

Jump Rope Times

Time (hours)	0.5	0.75	1.25	1.75
Frequency	3	4	3	2

Write and solve a problem that can be answered using the table above.

_____

_____

Answer: _____

5 This stem-and-leaf plot shows the numbers of pages Richard read each day for a week.

Pages Read

Stem	Leaves
1	6 7
2	5 8
3	1 3 5

1 | 6   represents 16

What is the sum of the greatest number of pages and the least number of pages Richard read?

Answer: _____

✂ -

Parent Activities

1. Collect data that shows how much liquid, to the nearest $\frac{1}{4}$ cup, each member of the family consumes in one day. Help your child show the data on a dot plot. Discuss the difference between the highest and lowest values and the total amount consumed by all family members.

2. Sort a collection of coins into quarters, dimes, nickels, and pennies. Create a frequency table and a dot plot to show the numbers of coins for each decimal value. Calculate the total value of the coin collection.

motivation**math**™
Performance Assessments

Performance Assessment A: Pie Palooza

Performance Assessment B: How Does Our Garden Grow?

motivation**math**™LEVEL 4

Problem Stimulus

"Let's enter the pie-eating contest at the Pie Palooza," said Jacob. "The winner receives four passes to the movies."

"That sounds like fun!" cried Sophia.

"You know how I love pie!" added Ethan.

"I'm getting hungry just thinking about it!" exclaimed Jon.

"What is the Pie Palooza?" asked Mia.

"It is an annual event in which the parents donate pies to raise money for our art program," answered Sophia. "There is always a pie-eating contest, and afterward there are lots of delicious pie slices for sale."

"It sounds messy to me," giggled Mia, "but I'll give it a try. Afterward, I'll take pictures with my new camera."

At the contest, five pies were lined up on the table. Five children took their places, each standing in front of a pie. "Look," said Sophia. "The pie tins for the contest are filled with whipped cream."

"That makes them easier to eat," declared Jacob.

"I was hoping for cherry pie," grumbled Ethan.

The judge announced, "You may not use your hands to eat your pie. You must place your hands behind your back. I'll tell you when to begin. When one minute has passed I'll blow the whistle, and the child who has eaten the greatest fraction of a pie is the winner. Ready? Go!"

The children began eating. Sophia lapped the whipped cream with her tongue. Jacob gulped big mouthfuls of the fluffy topping. Ethan buried his face into the mountain of soft whipped cream. He moved his head left and right, swallowing with every movement. They heard the whistle sound, ending the contest.

While the children washed their faces, the judge studied each pie plate and recorded fractions on a record sheet. According to the judge's records, Ethan ate $\frac{2}{3}$ of his pie, and Jacob ate $\frac{8}{12}$ of his pie. Mia ate $\frac{3}{4}$ of her pie, Jon ate $\frac{4}{5}$ of his pie, and Sophia ate $\frac{4}{6}$ of her pie.

Task Overview

Five friends are excited about the Pie Palooza fundraiser at their school. The parents donate pies to raise money for the art program. Solve these problems about the Pie Palooza event.

Performance Task

Part A

Use the information in the story to answer these questions.

1 The judge's records show that Ethan and Jacob each ate the same fraction of a pie. Ethan multiplies $\frac{2}{3}$ by a fraction equal to 1 to prove that his fraction is equivalent to Jacob's fraction. Write numbers in the boxes to show Ethan's work.

$$\frac{2}{3} \times \frac{\boxed{}}{\boxed{}} = \frac{8}{12}$$

Jacob divides $\frac{8}{12}$ by a fraction equal to 1 to prove his fraction is equivalent to Ethan's fraction. Write numbers in the boxes to show Jacob's work.

$$\frac{8}{12} \div \frac{\boxed{}}{\boxed{}} = \frac{2}{3}$$

2 The judge's records show that another student ate the same fraction of a pie as Ethan and Jacob. Which student tied with Ethan and Jacob?

Use words, numbers, or pictures to explain how you found your answer.

Part B

The pie booth sells pie by the slice. Jacob wants to purchase exactly $\frac{7}{8}$ of a pie. The pies are equal sizes and are all cut into 8 equal slices. The flavor choices and prices are shown on the sign.

Pie Palooza

1 slice of pie	$ 3
$\frac{1}{2}$ of a whole pie	$11
1 whole pie	$20

Flavor Choices

Apple	Lemon
Caramel	Pecan
Cherry	Pumpkin
Chocolate	Strawberry

One way Jacob can purchase $\frac{7}{8}$ of a pie is to purchase 1 slice of apple pie, 2 slices of chocolate pie, 3 slices of lemon pie, and 1 slice of pecan pie.

He represents his purchase with a drawing and an equation.

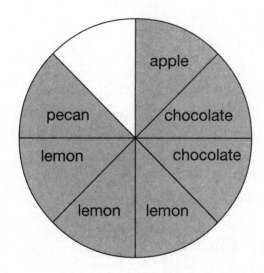

$$\frac{1}{8} + \frac{2}{8} + \frac{3}{8} + \frac{1}{8} = \frac{7}{8}$$

Performance Assessment A

1 What are three other ways Jacob can purchase $\frac{7}{8}$ of a pie with different flavors? For each answer, draw a picture and record an equation to justify your answer.

Answer 1:

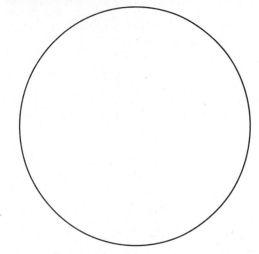

Equation _____

Answer 2:

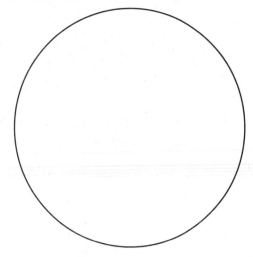

Equation _____

Answer 3:

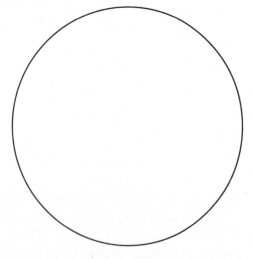

Equation _____

 motivation**math**™ LEVEL 4

2 Mia wants to purchase exactly $\frac{3}{4}$ of a pie. How many slices of pie should Mia purchase? Explain how you found your answer.

3 Ethan wants to purchase 8 slices of lemon pie to take home to his family. Explain how Ethan should purchase the pie in order to pay the lowest price.

4 Mrs. Johnson sliced and sold pie at the cherry and apple pie station. She began with 15 pies. She sold $5\frac{7}{8}$ cherry pies and $7\frac{5}{8}$ apple pies during the first hour of the Pie Palooza. Expressed as a mixed number, how many pies did Mrs. Johnson have left? Use numbers and pictures to show your answer.

Performance Assessment A

Part C

Use the given information to solve the problems.

1 After the fundraiser, one pie plate with $\frac{3}{8}$ of a lemon pie remained. Another pie plate contained $\frac{2}{8}$ of a lemon pie. Mrs. Johnson combined the remaining slices of pie into one pie plate. What fraction of the pie plate was filled? Draw a picture to justify your answer.

2 There were 5 slices of apple pie left in one pie plate and 2 slices left in another. Mrs. Johnson combined the slices into one plate. What fraction of the plate was empty? Draw a picture to show your answer.

Part D

Jon enjoyed the Pie Palooza so much that he organized a pie-eating contest for his Cub Scout den.

1 The table below shows the fraction of a whole pie eaten by each boy in the den. Use the fraction bars to help sort the fractions into 4 groups—closer to 0, closer to $\frac{1}{2}$, closer to $\frac{3}{4}$, and closer to 1.

Place an X in one column for each fraction of pie eaten.

Fractions of Pies Eaten

Name	Fraction of Pie Eaten	Closer to 0	Closer to $\frac{1}{2}$	Closer to $\frac{3}{4}$	Closer to 1
Mike	$\frac{6}{10}$				
Lance	$\frac{7}{9}$				
Julio	$\frac{3}{12}$				
Clarence	$\frac{1}{6}$				
Kevin	$\frac{11}{12}$				
Luke	$\frac{4}{5}$				

Fraction Bars

1 whole

$\frac{1}{2}$	$\frac{1}{2}$

$\frac{1}{3}$	$\frac{1}{3}$	$\frac{1}{3}$

$\frac{1}{4}$	$\frac{1}{4}$	$\frac{1}{4}$	$\frac{1}{4}$

$\frac{1}{5}$	$\frac{1}{5}$	$\frac{1}{5}$	$\frac{1}{5}$	$\frac{1}{5}$

$\frac{1}{6}$	$\frac{1}{6}$	$\frac{1}{6}$	$\frac{1}{6}$	$\frac{1}{6}$	$\frac{1}{6}$

$\frac{1}{8}$	$\frac{1}{8}$	$\frac{1}{8}$	$\frac{1}{8}$	$\frac{1}{8}$	$\frac{1}{8}$	$\frac{1}{8}$	$\frac{1}{8}$

$\frac{1}{9}$	$\frac{1}{9}$	$\frac{1}{9}$	$\frac{1}{9}$	$\frac{1}{9}$	$\frac{1}{9}$	$\frac{1}{9}$	$\frac{1}{9}$	$\frac{1}{9}$

$\frac{1}{10}$	$\frac{1}{10}$	$\frac{1}{10}$	$\frac{1}{10}$	$\frac{1}{10}$	$\frac{1}{10}$	$\frac{1}{10}$	$\frac{1}{10}$	$\frac{1}{10}$	$\frac{1}{10}$

$\frac{1}{12}$	$\frac{1}{12}$	$\frac{1}{12}$	$\frac{1}{12}$	$\frac{1}{12}$	$\frac{1}{12}$	$\frac{1}{12}$	$\frac{1}{12}$	$\frac{1}{12}$	$\frac{1}{12}$	$\frac{1}{12}$	$\frac{1}{12}$

Performance Assessment A

2 Julio correctly estimates that together, he and another scout ate almost $\frac{1}{2}$ pie. Who is the other scout? Explain how you found your answer.

3 Luke estimates that together, he and Lance ate about $1\frac{1}{2}$ pies. Do you agree with Luke's estimate? Circle your answer.

Yes   No

Explain your reasoning.

_____

_____

_____

_____

 motivation**math**™ LEVEL 4

4 Kevin estimates that he ate about $\frac{1}{2}$ pie more than Lance ate. Do you agree with Kevin's estimate? Circle your answer.

Yes   No

Explain your reasoning.

_____

_____

_____

_____

_____

motivation**math**™LEVEL 4

Name: _____

Performance Assessment A: Pie Palooza Scoring Rubric

Task	Score Point: 1 Undeveloped	Score Point: 2 Developing	Score Point: 3 Developed	Student's Score (Circle)
A.1 Record fractions to prove Ethan and Jacob ate the same amount of pie.	Student records the correct numerator or denominator for at least 1 fraction.	Student records the correct numerator and denominator for 1 fraction.	Student records the correct numerator and denominator for each fraction.	Score: 1 2 3
A.2 Name the student who ate a fraction of pie equivalent to Ethan's and Jacob's fractions, and explain.	Student provides the correct name but does not record an explanation.	Student provides the correct name and attempts an explanation, but the explanation is not clear.	Student provides the correct name and records a clear explanation.	Score: 1 2 3
B.1 Show 3 ways Jacob can purchase $\frac{7}{8}$ of a pie with a picture and an equation.	Student records 1 correct answer, including a picture and an equation.	Student records 2 correct answers, including a picture and an equation for each.	Student records 3 correct answers, including a picture and an equation for each.	Score: 1 2 3
B.2 Determine how many slices of pie Mia should purchase, and explain.	Student uses a correct method for writing the equivalent fraction but records an incorrect answer due to a computation error.	Student records the correct answer, but the explanation is not clear.	Student records the correct answer and a clear explanation.	Score: 1 2 3
B.3 Explain how Ethan can purchase 8 slices of pie at the lowest price.	Student records correct computation, but arrives at an incorrect answer.	Student records the correct answer, but the explanation is not clear.	Student records the correct answer and a clear explanation.	Score: 1 2 3
B.4 Determine how many pies Mrs. Johnson had left.	Student attempts to add the mixed numbers and then subtract from 15, but records an incorrect answer due to a computation error.	Student solves either the addition or subtraction problem correctly, but the answer is incorrect due to a computation error in the other step.	Student records the correct answer.	Score: 1 2 3

Task	Score Point: 1 Undeveloped	Score Point: 2 Developing	Score Point: 3 Developed	Student's Score (Circle)
C.1 Determine and draw a picture to represent the fraction of the pie plate that was filled.	Student draws a picture, but records an incorrect answer due to an error in the picture.	Student draws a correct picture, but records an incorrect answer.	Student draws a correct picture and records the correct answer.	Score: 1 2 3
C.2 Determine and draw a picture to represent the fraction of the pie plate that was empty.	Student draws a picture, but does not solve any part of the problem correctly.	Student draws an accurate picture and determines that the pie plate was $\frac{7}{8}$ full, but student does not record the correct solution to the problem.	Student draws an accurate picture and records the correct solution to the problem.	Score: 1 2 3
D.1 Sort the fractions into 4 groups.	Student accurately sorts 1 or 2 fractions.	Student accurately sorts 3–5 fractions.	Student accurately sorts 6 fractions.	Score: 1 2 3
D.2 Determine the student whose fraction of eaten pie, when added to Julio's fraction, equals about $\frac{1}{2}$. Explain the answer.	Student records an incorrect answer.	Student records the correct answer, but the explanation is not clear.	Student records the correct answer and a clear explanation.	Score: 1 2 3
D.3 Determine whether Luke's estimate is reasonable, and explain.	Student disagrees with Luke.	Student agrees with Luke, but the explanation is not clear.	Student agrees with Luke and clearly explains reasoning.	Score: 1 2 3
D.4 Determine whether Kevin's estimate is reasonable and explain.	Student agrees with Kevin.	Student disagrees with Kevin, but the explanation is not clear.	Student disagrees with Kevin and clearly explains reasoning.	Score: 1 2 3
			Student's Total Score	

32–36 points = Proficient   27–31 points = Satisfactory   19–26 points = Below Standard   0–18 points = Unsatisfactory

motivation**math**™ LEVEL 4

Problem Stimulus

Mr. Shaye stood in front of his fourth-grade class. "We have an interesting opportunity," he said to his twenty-five students. "The PTA® is sponsoring a program at our school that allows students to make a contribution to PATH. I'm sure many of you are familiar with this organization – People Attempting to Help. PATH provides food, clothing, and other assistance to families in need. One PATH program accepts donations of fresh fruits and vegetables. This year, PATH is asking schools to participate by encouraging classes to plant vegetable gardens and donate the food they grow. I thought our class might want to participate."

The classroom buzzed with the sound of students' voices. Mr. Shaye continued, "The principal said that each participating class can plant a garden at the far end of the school grounds. Each class will be responsible for planning, planting, and maintaining its own garden. We would also need to fertilize, water, and weed the garden as well as harvest the vegetables. What are your thoughts? Are we in?"

"I think it's a great idea," said Sloan. "Who says kids can't make a difference?"

"When would we do all this?" questioned Nate. "During school hours or after school?"

"What difference does it make?" replied Amy. "I agree with Sloan. This is a way for us to give something back. I say we go for it."

The other students nodded in agreement. "I thought you'd like the idea," Mr. Shaye said. "I have a few thoughts, but I want yours as well. I have 12 yards of fencing left from building a dog pen. We can use that to fence the area for our garden. I'll donate the fencing. I'll even volunteer to come on Saturday to install the fence around our garden plot. Mrs. Spence, the PTA® president, gave the teachers a price list from Adams Seed and Feed. It shows prices for plants and fertilizer. Mrs. Spence said that each class that participates will be allowed to spend up to $75 on materials. We need to decide which vegetables to plant and how we'll tend the garden."

Will's hand shot up. "I have an idea," he said. "There are twenty-five of us in the class. We could divide into five teams. Each team would be responsible for tending the garden one school day each week."

"I like your thinking, Will," Mr. Shaye replied. "What about weekends though?"

Amy chimed in, "Maybe those of us who live close to the school could come on weekends with our parents. I know my family would come with me."

"You're great problem solvers," Mr. Shaye chuckled. "I guess twenty-five heads are better than one!" The class laughed. "Tell you what," he continued, "I'll make copies of the price list, and we can begin planning."

"What do we need to do first?" Matt questioned. "You know, something like this takes a lot of planning. My mom always says that if you fail to plan, then you're planning to fail."

Performance Assessment B

Mr. Shaye agreed, "And she's right, Matt. Why don't we get together in discussion groups and brainstorm? We can make lists of all the things we need to consider, and then compile one big list and make decisions."

The students got to work immediately. After the brainstorming session, each group reported their ideas. Mr. Shaye compiled his students' ideas into one list on the dry-erase board.

Things to Consider

1. Determine the size of the garden.
2. Decide how many sections will be in the garden.
3. Decide which vegetables to plant.
4. Decide what brand of fertilizer to use.
5. Determine groups to tend the garden each day.

"We have a great start on this project," Mr. Shaye told his students. "And I just had another idea. We will begin our study of measurement in math next week. We can combine this gardening project with our math unit by keeping track of the growth of our plants."

"I knew you'd find a way to tie this to math!" Jason exclaimed. "Good thing math is my favorite subject!"

"Hey, my dad owns a landscaping company," Nate said. "I bet he'd let us use some of his tools and stuff."

Amy added, "Yeah, and maybe some sprinklers and hoses, too! I guess we can't depend on Mother Nature to supply all the water!"

Together, the class made decisions about the garden. They knew that the perimeter of the garden would be 12 yards, since that was the amount of fencing available. The class agreed that, in order to keep the garden manageable, they would divide it into four equal sections and plant a different vegetable in each section. As students poured over the price list from Adams Seed and Feed, they made decisions about fertilizer, which vegetables to plant, and how to best tend the garden. Matt created a table on his computer to keep track of the costs. Mr. Shaye ordered the plants and fertilizer from Adams Seed and Feed.

The following week, the class staked out their garden. Mr. Shaye, with the help of some class dads, put the fence around the perimeter of the garden. Nate's dad tilled the soil. The students spread fertilizer and planted the seedling plants. As the weeks passed, Mr. Shaye and his students carefully tended their garden plot. Finally, they reaped the bounty of the garden. The students all agreed that, while it was a lot of work, the gardening project was a huge success. When they made the presentation to PATH, the director complimented the class, "I'm proud to award a blue ribbon to a class with green thumbs!"

Name _____

midHow Does Our Garden Grow?

Performance Assessment B

Adams Seed and Feed
3265 Highway 64
Hawthorne, Texas 73737
555.YOU.GROW

Serving Hawthorne's finest gardeners since 1975

Fertilizers

Fertilizer for Vegetable Gardens

Brand	Weight (pounds)	Coverage (square feet)	Price (per bag)
Adams Best	3	70	$5
Healthy Plant	4	84	$8
Veg-a-Lize	6	90	$7
Veggie-Grow	2	50	$3

Plants

Vegetable Seedling Plants

Vegetable	Approximate Space Needed per plant (square feet)	Price (per plant)
Cabbage	2	$2
Cauliflower	1	$1
Cherry Tomatoes	4	$2
Cucumber	4	$3
Green Peppers	2	$3
Lettuce	1	$1
Large Tomatoes	5	$3
Squash	5	$2
Turnips	2	$2

At Adams Seed and Feed, we're always on the grow.

Task Overview

Mr. Shaye's fourth-grade class wants to plant a vegetable garden and donate the vegetables to PATH, a local organization that helps people in need. The students plan their garden and agree on some specific guidelines. Use information from the story, the price list from Adams Seed and Feed, and the diagram of plant heights to answer the questions.

Performance Task

Part A

1 The students know that the perimeter of the garden must be 12 yards. How many feet is this? Show your work.

2 How many inches are in 12 yards? Show your work.

3 Complete the conversion table to convert the measurements given.

Conversion Table

Yards	Feet	Inches
1	3	36
	6	
	12	
	24	
12		
	45	
20		

motivation**math**™LEVEL 4

How Does Our Garden Grow?

Part B

1 Use the number of feet in 12 yards to draw all possible rectangular gardens with whole number sides lengths that could be created with this perimeter. Name the gardens A, B, C, D, etc. Label the length and width of each garden, in feet.

2 Record the area of each garden, in square feet, below its rectangular model.

Performance Assessment B

Part C

1 The students decide to divide the garden into four equal areas. Use the square foot areas you found in question B.2 to determine which of the rectangular gardens you sketched in question B.1 can be divided into four equal sections with whole number areas. Write the letter names of the gardens that meet this requirement.

2 Of the gardens you identified in question C.1, which single garden provides the greatest area of growing space in each section?

3 Use the garden you identified in question C.2 to sketch four possible ways this garden could be divided into 4 equal sections for planting vegetables.

4 How many square feet will be in each section of this garden?

 motivation**math**™LEVEL 4

Part D

1 Mr. Shaye's class decides to grow a different vegetable in each of the four garden sections. The PTA® agreed to provide each class with up to $75 to purchase fertilizer and plants. Matt created a table to keep track of the costs. Study the price list from Adams Seed and Feed to determine a combination of plants and fertilizer the class could purchase and not exceed $75. Then complete Matt's table to show how you would recommend spending the $75. You must spend at least $65, but must not exceed the $75 limit.

Class Garden Costs

Item	Number Needed	Price per Item	Total Cost
		Total Amount Spent	

Performance Assessment B

Part E

1 Mr. Shaye's students decided to track the growth of 10 plants over an 8-week period to determine which plants were the fastest growing. Using a customary ruler, measure the heights of the seedling plants to the nearest $\frac{1}{4}$ inch. Record the data on the table.

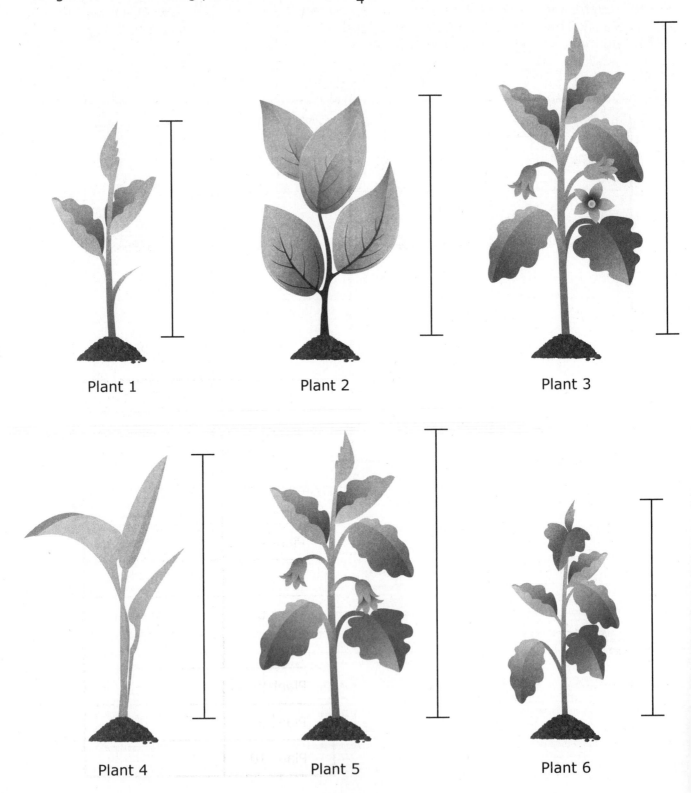

Plant 1   Plant 2   Plant 3

Plant 4   Plant 5   Plant 6

How Does Our Garden Grow?

Plant 7

Plant 8

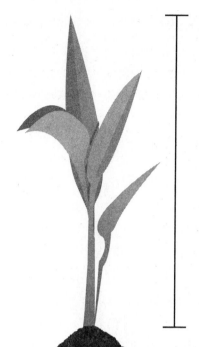

Plant 9

Plant 10

Seedling Heights

Plant	Height (inches)
Plant 1	
Plant 2	
Plant 3	
Plant 4	
Plant 5	
Plant 6	
Plant 7	
Plant 8	
Plant 9	
Plant 10	

Performance Assessment B

2 In the space below, create a dot plot to display the set of data from question E.1. Be sure to title your dot plot and label the parts.

3 Which seedling measurement is recorded most often?

4 How many seedlings are greater than 2 inches in height but less than 3 inches in height?

5 What is the difference in height between one of the tallest and the shortest seedlings?

6 If all the seedlings that measure greater than $2\frac{3}{4}$ inches in height were placed end to end, what would be the total height? Show your work.

Performance Assessment B: How Does Our Garden Grow? Scoring Rubric

Name: _____

Task	Score Point: 1 Undeveloped	Score Point: 2 Developing	Score Point: 3 Developed	Student's Score (Circle)
A.1 How many feet are in 12 yards? Show all work.	The student attempts to compute the number of feet in 12 yards, but does not find the correct answer and fails to show all work.	The student attempts to compute the number of feet in 12 yards and shows all work, but makes a computation error.	The student correctly computes the number of feet in 12 yards and shows all work.	Score: 1 2 3
A.2 How many inches are in 12 yards? Show all work.	The student attempts to compute the number of inches in 12 yards, but does not find the correct answer and fails to show all work.	The student attempts to compute the number of inches in 12 yards and shows all work, but makes a computation error.	The student correctly computes the number of inches in 12 yards and shows all work.	Score: 1 2 3
A.3 Complete the conversion table to convert the measurements given.	The student correctly calculates fewer than 7 of 12 conversions on the table.	The student correctly calculates 7–9 of the 12 conversions on the table.	The student correctly calculates 10 or more conversions on the table.	Score: 1 2 3
B.1 Use the number of feet in 12 yards to draw all possible rectangular gardens that could be created with this perimeter. Name the gardens A, B, C, D, etc. Label the length and width of each garden, in feet.	The student correctly draws and names less than half of the possible rectangles with the specified perimeter. The student does not label the length and width of each model.	The student correctly draws and names approximately 75–90% of the possible rectangles with the specified perimeter. The student labels the length and width of each model.	The student correctly draws and names 90–100% of the possible rectangles with the specified perimeter. The student labels the length and width of each model.	Score: 1 2 3
B.2 Record the area of each garden, in square feet, below each rectangular model.	The student correctly labels less than half the possible models with the correct area, in square feet.	The student correctly labels at least 75–90% of the models with the correct area, in square feet.	The student correctly labels 90–100% of the models with the correct area, in square feet.	Score: 1 2 3

Task	Score Point: 1 Undeveloped	Score Point: 2 Developing	Score Point: 3 Developed	Student's Score (Circle)
C.1 Write the letter names of the gardens that can be divided into four equal sections with whole number areas.	The student correctly identifies less than half of the possible gardens that meet the criteria.	The student correctly identifies all but one of the possible gardens that meet the criteria.	The student correctly identifies all possible gardens that meet the criteria.	Score: 1 2 3
C.2 Which single garden provides the greatest area of growing space in each section?	The student attempts to identify the single garden with the greatest area of growing space, but is unsuccessful.		The student correctly identifies the garden with the greatest area of growing space.	Score: 1 2 3
C.3/C.4 Sketch four possible ways the garden identified in C.2 could be divided into 4 equal sections for planting vegetables. Identify the number of square feet in each section.	The student correctly sketches 1 or 2 of four possible ways the garden could be divided into 4 equal sections. The student incorrectly identifies the number of square feet.	The student correctly sketches 3 of 4 possible ways the garden could be divided into 4 equal sections and identifies the number of square feet.	The student correctly sketches 4 possible ways the garden could be divided into 4 equal sections and identifies the number of square feet.	Score: 1 2 3
D.1 Complete Matt's table to show how you would recommend spending the $75. You must spend at least $65, but must not exceed the $75 limit.	The student is unable to complete the table and/or shows multiple errors in meeting the designated criteria: • 4 different plants • at least 1 fertilizer • stay within $65–$75 total expenditures.	The student completes the table, but shows errors in meeting 1 of the designated criteria: • 4 different plants • at least 1 fertilizer • stay within $65–$75 total expenditures.	The student completes the table and meets all designated criteria: • 4 different plants • at least 1 fertilizer • stay within $65–$75 total expenditures.	Score: 1 2 3
E.1 Using a customary ruler, measure the heights of the seedling plants to the nearest $\frac{1}{4}$ inch. Record ...n the table	The student correctly measures and records the heights of fewer than 6 of the 10 plants shown.	The student correctly measures and records the heights of 6–8 of the 10 plants shown.	The student correctly measures and records the heights of 9 or 10 of the 10 plants shown.	Score: 1 2 3

motivation**math**™ LEVEL 4

Task	Score Point: 1 Undeveloped	Score Point: 2 Developing	Score Point: 3 Developed	Student's Score (Circle)
E.2 Create a dot plot to display the set of data from question E.1. Be sure to title your dot plot and label the parts.	The student attempts to create the dot plot and represents 6 or fewer of 10 data points correctly. The student does not provide a title and/or labels.	The student correctly creates the dot plot and represents 7–9 of 10 data points correctly. The student provides a title and labels.	The student correctly creates the dot plot and represents all 10 data points correctly. The student provides a title and labels.	Score: 1 2 3
E.3 Which seedling measurement is recorded most often? E.4 How many seedlings are greater than 2 inches in height but less than 3 inches in height?	The student attempts to answer both questions, but does not correctly answer either one.	The student attempts to answer both questions, but correctly answers only 1 of the 2 questions.	The student correctly answers both questions.	Score: 1 2 3
E.5 What is the difference in height between one of the tallest and the shortest seedlings? Show all work.	The student attempts to calculate the answer to the question, but is unable to find the correct answer and does not show his/her work.	The student attempts to calculate the answer to the question and shows his/her work, but derives an incorrect answer.	The student correctly calculates the answer to the question and shows his/her work.	Score: 1 2 3
E.6 If all the seedlings that measure greater than $2\frac{3}{4}$ inches in height were placed end to end, what would be the total height? Show all work.	The student attempts to calculate the total height, but does not show all work and derives an incorrect answer.	The student attempts to calculate the total height and shows all work, but derives an incorrect answer.	The student correctly calculates the total height and shows all work.	Score: 1 2 3
			Student's Total Score	

38–42 points = Proficient   30–37 points = Satisfactory   25–29 points = Below Standard   Below 25 points = Unsatisfactory

motivation**math**™LEVEL 4

Chart Your Success

Color Mike or Molly **green** if your answer was correct or **red** if your answer was incorrect.

									Total Correct	Total Possible
Unit 1 Page **10**	Use Base 10 Place Value 4.2(A)	1	2	3	4	5	6			**6**
Unit 2 Page **18**	Represent the Value of Digits 4.2(B)	1	2	3	4	5				**5**
Unit 3 Page **26**	Compare and Order Whole Numbers 4.2(C)	1	2	3	4	5				**5**
Unit 4 Page **34**	Round Whole Numbers 4.2(D)	1	2	3	4	5				**5**
Unit 5 Page **42**	Represent Decimals 4.2(E)	1	2	3	4					**4**
Unit 6 Page **50**	Compare and Order Decimals 4.2(F)	1	2	3	4					**4**
Unit 7 Page **58**	Relate Decimals to Fractions 4.2(G)	1	2	3	4	5	6			**6**
Unit 8 Page **66**	Represent Decimals on a Number Line 4.2(H)	1	2	3	4	5				**5**
Unit 9 Page **74**	Decompose Fractions 4.3(A), 4.3(B)	1	2	3	4					**4**
Unit 10 Page **82**	Determine Equivalent Fractions 4.3(C)	1	2	3	4	5				**5**
Unit 11 Page **90**	Compare Fractions 4.3(D)	1	2	3	4	5				**5**
Unit 12 Page **98**	Solve Problems: +/− Fractions 4.3(E)	1	2	3	4					**4**
Unit 13 Page **06**	Evaluate Reasonableness: +/− Fractions 4.3(F)	1	2	3	4	5	6			**6**

Chart Your Success

Color Mike or Molly **green** if your answer was correct or **red** if your answer was incorrect.

Unit / Page	Skill	1	2	3	4	5	6		Total Correct	Total Possible
Unit 14 Page **114**	Represent Fractions and Decimals on Number Lines 4.3(G)	☺	☺	☺	☺	☺			Total Correct	Total Possible **5**
Unit 15 Page **122**	Add and Subtract Whole Numbers and Decimals 4.4(A)	☺	☺	☺	☺	☺			Total Correct	Total Possible **5**
Unit 16 Page **130**	Multiply by 10 or 100 4.4(B)	☺	☺	☺	☺	☺			Total Correct	Total Possible **5**
Unit 17 Page **138**	Represent Products: Arrays, Area Models, and Equations 4.4(C)	☺	☺	☺	☺				Total Correct	Total Possible **4**
Unit 18 Page **146**	Multiply Using Strategies and Algorithms 4.4(D)	☺	☺	☺	☺	☺	☺		Total Correct	Total Possible **6**
Unit 19 Page **154**	Represent Quotients: Arrays, Area Models, and Equations 4.4(E)	☺	☺	☺	☺				Total Correct	Total Possible **4**
Unit 20 Page **162**	Divide Using Strategies and Algorithms 4.4(F)	☺	☺	☺	☺	☺			Total Correct	Total Possible **5**
Unit 21 Page **170**	Estimate Solutions: Whole Numbers 4.4(G)	☺	☺	☺	☺	☺	☺		Total Correct	Total Possible **6**
Unit 22 Page **178**	Solve One- and Two-Step Problems: ×/÷ 4.4(H)	☺	☺	☺	☺	☺	☺		Total Correct	Total Possible **6**
Unit 23 Page **186**	Solve Multi-step Problems: +, −, ×, ÷ 4.5(A)	☺	☺	☺	☺	☺			Total Correct	Total Possible **5**
Unit 24 Page **194**	Generate Number Patterns: Input/Output Tables 4.5(B)	☺	☺	☺	☺				Total Correct	Total Possible **4**
Unit 25 Page **202**	Solve Problems: Perimeter and Area 4.5(C), 4.5(D)	☺	☺	☺	☺	☺			Total Correct	Total Possible **5**
Unit 26 Page **210**	Identify Points, Lines, and Angles 4.6(A)	☺	☺	☺	☺	☺			Total Correct	Total Possible **5**

ILLEGAL TO COPY   motivation**math**-LEVEL 4   ©2014 mentoring**minds**.co

Chart Your Success

Color Mike or Molly **green** if your answer was correct or **red** if your answer was incorrect.

Unit / Page	Skill	Questions						Total Correct	Total Possible
Unit 27 Page 218	Identify and Draw Lines of Symmetry 4.6(B)	1	2	3	4	5		Total Correct	**5**
Unit 28 Page 226	Identify Acute, Right, and Obtuse Triangles 4.6(C)	1	2	3	4	5		Total Correct	**5**
Unit 29 Page 234	Use Lines and Angles to Classify Figures 4.6(D)	1	2	3	4	5		Total Correct	**5**
Unit 30 Page 242	Illustrate Angle Measures in Degrees 4.7(A), 4.7(B)	1	2	3	4			Total Correct	**4**
Unit 31 Page 250	Measure and Draw Angles 4.7(C), 4.7(D)	1	2	3	4	5	6	Total Correct	**6**
Unit 32 Page 258	Determine Angle Measures: Adjacent Angles 4.7(E)	1	2	3	4			Total Correct	**4**
Unit 33 Page 266	Identify Measurement Units and Convert Measures 4.8(A), 4.8(B)	1	2	3	4	5		Total Correct	**5**
Unit 34 Page 274	Solve Problems: Measurement 4.8(C)	1	2	3	4	5	6	Total Correct	**6**
Unit 35 Page 282	Represent Data on Tables and Plots 4.9(A)	1	2					Total Correct	**2**
Unit 36 Page 290	Solve Problems: Data from Tables and Plots 4.9(B)	1	2	3	4	5		Total Correct	**5**
Unit 37 Page 298	Classify Expenses and Calculate Profit 4.10(A), 4.10(B)	1	2	3	4	5		Total Correct	**5**
Unit 38 Page 306	Describe Savings Options, Spending, and Financial Institutions 4.10(C), 4.10(D), 4.10(E)	1	2	3	4	5		Total Correct	**5**

motivation**math**™LEVEL 4

Math Glossary

A

acute angle – an angle measuring less than 90°

acute triangle – a triangle with three acute angles

add/addition – (*verb*) to combine two or more groups; (*noun*) the operation used to combine groups to find the total amount or sum

addends – numbers that are added

adjacent angles – two or more angles that share a common ray, have a common vertex, and do not overlap

algorithm – a step-by-step process for solving a problem

allowance – an amount of money paid regularly in exchange for completing chores or assigned tasks; often paid by a parent to a child

angle – the figure formed by 2 rays that extend from a common endpoint

approximate – (*verb*) to estimate or come close to; (*adj*ective) almost exact or correct

area – the number of square units needed to cover a surface

area model – a replica or figure used to represent area

array – an arrangement of objects in equal rows and columns

associative property – a property of addition or multiplication in which the grouping of the addends or factors does not change the outcome of the operation, such as $(1 + 2) + 3 = 1 + (2 + 3)$ and $(1 \times 2) \times 3 = 1 \times (2 \times 3)$

attribute – a characteristic or property of a shape or thing

B

bank – a financial institution that allows customers to open checking or savings accounts and borrow money; banks make a profit by charging fees or interest

bar graph – a graph that uses horizontal or vertical bars to represent data

base-10 place value system – a numbering system based on 10 in which the value of each place is 10 times as much as the place to its right and $\frac{1}{10}$ the value of the place to its left

benchmark fraction – a fraction used to judge the approximate size of another fraction; benchmark fractions may include $\frac{1}{4}$, $\frac{1}{2}$, and $\frac{3}{4}$; for example knowing that $\frac{3}{8}$ is close to $\frac{4}{8}$ (or $\frac{1}{2}$), helps to understand the approximate size of the fraction $\frac{3}{8}$ as a little less than half

borrow – to obtain or use money from a bank or other person in order to purchase goods or services

budget – an organized plan, developed by a person, family, or business, for spending and saving money; budgets help people better manage money and make wise decisions involving income, spending, savings, and charitable giving

C

capacity – the amount of liquid a container can hold; also known as liquid volume; may be measured in fluid ounces, pints, quarts, gallons, milliliters, or liters

categorical data – observations that can be sorted into groups or categories such as shoe colors or favorite vegetables

center (of a circle) – the exact middle of a circle from which all points on the circumference are the same distance

centimeter (cm) – a metric unit used to measure length

certificate of deposit (CD) – a savings certificate that is issued by a bank or other financial institution in exchange for depositing money for a specific amount of time; a CD earns a higher rate of interest than a regular savings account, but a penalty is charged if money is withdrawn early

charity – an organization that helps people who are poor, ill, or have special needs

checking account – an account at a bank that allows a person to deposit or withdraw money and write checks to pay for goods and services

circle – a two-dimensional figure consisting of a closed curve with all points the same distance from the center

coin – metal disks used as money; the most common U.S. coins and their values include penny (1¢), nickel (5¢), dime (10¢), quarter (25¢), and half-dollar (50¢)

common denominator – a denominator that is the same in two or more fractions

commutative property – a property of addition or multiplication in which the sum or product stays the same when the order of the addends or factors is changed, such as $3 + 4 = 4 + 3$ and $5 \times 2 = 2 \times 5$

compare – to determine whether two or more numbers or quantities are greater than, less than, or equal to one another

compatible numbers – pairs of numbers that can easily be computed mentally, such as $23 + 27$ is close to $25 + 25$, so the estimate is 50; $3,720 \div 6$ is close to $3,600 \div 6$, so the estimate is 600

compose – to join numbers to create tens, hundreds, thousands, etc.; to join or put together parts to create a whole

congruent – figures that are the same size and same shape

convert (measurement) – to change from one measurement unit to another using a conversion factor; for example, converting feet to inches requires multiplying the number of feet $\times$ 12

cost – the amount paid for goods and services based on their value

credit union – a financial institution that is owned by its members; a credit union may offer options for savings accounts and loans to its members; credit unions do not operate to make a profit, so they may offer lower interest rates on loans

cup (c) – a customary unit equal to 8 fluid ounces; used to measure liquid volume (capacity)

customary system of measurement – the measurement system used most often in the United States

D

data – a collection of facts or information gathered by observing, questioning, or measuring; usually displayed on a chart, table, or graph

decimal number – a number that uses a decimal point to show tenths or hundredths

decimal point – the dot used to separate the ones place from the tenths place in a decimal number

decompose – to break down or break apart into smaller parts

degree (of an angle) – a unit used to measure the size of angles; the symbol for degree is °

denominator – the bottom number in a fraction; the total number of equal parts

deposit – money placed into a checking or savings account at a bank

difference – the answer to a subtraction problem

digit – one of the symbols 0, 1, 2, 3, 4, 5, 6, 7, 8, and 9 used to write numbers

dimension – measurement of a geometric shape in one direction

distance – the length between two specific points

distributive property – multiplying a number by a sum is the same as multiplying the number by each addend of the sum and then adding the products, such as $2 \times (3 + 4) = (2 \times 3) + (2 \times 4)$

divide/division – (*verb*) to separate into equal parts or equal groups; (*noun*) the operation of making equal groups to find the number in each group or to find the number of equal groups

dividend – the number to be divided in a division problem

 motivation**math**™ LEVEL 4 ©2014 mentoring**minds**.cor

divisibility rules – patterns used to determine whether a number divides evenly into another number without actually completing the division

divisible – when a number can be divided by another number with no remainder, such as 12 is divisible by 3

divisor – the number by which another number is divided

donate – to give money or other resources to help others

donation – something of value that is given to a charitable organization; donations may be in the form of money, goods, or services

dot plot – a graph that uses dots above a number line to show the frequency of data

E

earn – to work in exchange for payment

earned income – money received in exchange for work; earnings may include salary, tips, fees, or interest earned on savings accounts

elapsed time – the amount of time that passes from the start of an activity to the end of that activity

endpoint – a point at the end of a line segment or ray

equal parts – parts of a whole that are the same size

equal sign (=) – the symbol used to show that two sets or expressions are exactly the same in amount or value

equation – a number sentence that uses the equal sign to show that two expressions are equal

equivalent – the same in value or amount

equivalent fractions – two or more fractions that are equal

estimate – (*noun*) an answer that is close to the exact answer; (*verb*) to guess about

expanded notation – a way to write numbers that shows the value of each digit

expense – an amount of money used to buy goods or services

expression – a mathematical combination of numbers, operations, and variables

F

fact family – a set of related number sentences

factor – a number that is multiplied by another number to find a product

financial institution – a business that deals with money, deposits, investments, and loans, rather than goods or services

fixed expense – a cost that is the same each month and that cannot be easily adjusted to balance a budget, such as a car payment or rent

fluid ounce (fl oz) – a customary unit used to measure small amounts of liquid volume (capacity)

foot/feet (ft) – a customary unit equal to 12 inches; used to measure length

formula – a mathematical rule expressed in numbers and symbols

fraction – a number that names a part of a whole or part of a group

fraction bar – the horizontal line that separates the numerator from the denominator in a fraction

frequency – the number of times an event happens

frequency table – a table listing each value that appears in a data set followed by the number of times it appears

G

gallon (gal) – a customary unit equal to 4 quarts, 8 pints, or 16 cups; used to measure liquid volume (capacity)

gram (g) – a metric unit used to measure mass

greater than (>) – the symbol used to compare two numbers in which the larger number is on the left

21 > 13 means 21 is greater than 13

H

hexagon – a polygon with six sides and six angles

hour – a unit equal to 60 minutes; used to measure time

hundredth – one of 100 equal parts in a whole; the second place to the right of the decimal point

I

improper fraction – a fraction in which the numerator is greater than or equal to the denominator

inch (in.) – a customary unit used to measure length

income – the amount of money received in a particular time (weekly, monthly, yearly) in exchange for work

input-output table – a table of values that follows a rule; for each value used as an input, a rule is applied that results in a corresponding value as the output

insurance – an arrangement in which a company or organization guarantees the safety or security of money, life, or property against loss, damage, or injury; banks offer financial insurance to depositors to guarantee that their money is safe

interest – money paid by a borrower in exchange for using a lender's money for a certain period of time

intersect – to cross at a common point

intersecting lines – two lines that cross at exactly one point

K

kilogram (kg) – a metric unit equal to 1,000 grams; used to measure mass

kilometer (km) – a metric unit equal to 1,000 meters; used to measure length or distance

L

lend – to allow someone to use something, such as money or property, for a period of time with the understanding that it will be returned, often with interest

lender – a person or business that loans money

length – the distance from one end of an object to the other

less than ($<$) – the symbol used to compare two numbers when the smaller number is on the left
$14 < 29$ means 14 is less than 29

like denominators – in fractions, denominators that have the same value; $\frac{5}{8}$ and $\frac{7}{8}$ have like denominators

line – a straight path that extends infinitely in opposite directions

line of symmetry – a line that divides a figure into halves, forming a mirror image

line segment – a part of a line with two endpoints

liquid volume – the amount of space occupied by a pourable substance; also known as capacity; may be measured in fluid ounces, pints, quarts, gallons, milliliters, or liters

liter (L) – a metric unit equal to 1,000 milliliters; used to measure liquid volume (capacity)

loss – losing money or value

M

mass – the measure of the amount of matter in an object; gravity does not affect mass

measure – to find the size, weight/mass, or capacity of an item using a given unit

meter (m) – a metric unit equal to 100 centimeters or 1,000 millimeters; used to measure length

metric system of measurement – a measurement system used throughout the world, based on multiples of 10

midpoint – the point on a line segment that divides it into two congruent parts

mile (mi) – a customary unit equal to 1,760 yards or 5,280 feet; used to measure length or distance

milligram (mg) – a metric unit used to measure mass

milliliter (mL) – a metric unit used to measure liquid volume (capacity)

millimeter (mm) – a metric unit used to measure length

minute – a unit equal to 60 seconds; used to measure time

mixed number – a number composed of a whole number and a fraction, such as $2\frac{3}{4}$, $5\frac{1}{8}$, etc.

model – a drawing, diagram, or smaller version of something that represents the actual object

money market account – an account, similar to a checking account, that earns interest for the owner; deposits may be added at any time, but penalties may be assessed for frequent withdrawals

multiple – the product of a given number and any whole number
   Multiples of 5 include 5, 10, 15, 20, ...

multiply/multiplication – (*verb*) to join or combine equal groups; (*noun*) the operation using repeated addition of the same number; combining equal groups

N

number line – a line on which points correspond to numbers

number sentence – a mathematical sentence that uses numbers and symbols

numerator – the top number in a fraction; how many equal parts are being considered

O

obtuse angle – an angle measuring more than 90° but less than 180°

obtuse triangle – a triangle that has one angle with a measure greater than 90°

operation – an arithmetic procedure used to solve a mathematical problem, such as addition, subtraction, multiplication, or division

ounce (oz) – a customary unit used to measure weight

P

parallel – never meeting or intersecting; always the same distance apart

parallel lines – two lines in the same plane that never intersect

parallelogram – a quadrilateral with opposite sides that are parallel and congruent

partial product – when multiplying by a multi-digit multiplier, the result obtained when a factor is multiplied by the value of one of the digits

pattern – a regularly repeated arrangement of numbers, letters, or shapes

pentagon – a polygon with five sides and five angles

perimeter – the distance around a 2-dimensional figure

perpendicular – intersecting at right angles

perpendicular lines – lines that intersect to form right angles

pint (pt) – a customary unit equal to 2 cups; used to measure liquid volume (capacity)

place value – the value determined by the position of a digit in a number

point – an exact location or position; a point may be represented by a dot

polygon – a closed figure made of line segments

pound (lb) – a customary unit equal to 16 ounces; used to measure weight

product – the answer to a multiplication problem

profit – money that is left after paying all fixed and variable expenses; profit may be calculated by subtracting all costs from revenue

protractor – a tool used to measure angles

Q

quadrilateral – a polygon with four sides and four angles

quart (qt) – a customary unit equal to 2 pints or 4 cups; used to measure liquid volume (capacity)

quotient – the answer to a division problem

R

ray – a part of a line that has one endpoint and extends infinitely in the other direction

reasonable – logical or sensible

rectangle – a parallelogram with four right angles

regroup – to rename a number, such as 10 ones = 1 ten, 10 tens = 1 hundred

regular polygon – a polygon in which all sides are the same length and all angles have the same measure

relationship – a connection or pattern found between numbers

remainder – the number left over after dividing into equal groups

revenue – money a business receives from selling goods or services

rhombus – a parallelogram in which four sides are congruent and opposite angles are congruent

right angle – an angle with a measure of 90°

right triangle – a triangle with one right angle

round – to approximate a number to a given place value

rule – a procedure that a pattern must follow

S

salary – a set payment that a person receives in exchange for work performed

savings account – a bank account that allows a customer to deposit and withdraw money and earn interest from the bank

second – a unit used to measure small amounts of time

side – one of the line segments that forms a polygon

spend – to use money or other resources to pay for goods or services

square – a special rectangle with four sides of equal measure

square unit – a square with a side length of one unit that is used to measure area; square units may include square inch, square foot, square centimeter, and square meter

standard form – a number written with one digit for each place value

stem-and-leaf plot – a display of data in which digits with larger place values are named as stems and digits with smaller place values are named as leaves

straight angle – an angle with a measure of 180°

strip diagram – a model or drawing that looks like a strip of tape; a strip diagram is used to represent number relationships

subtract/subtraction – (*verb*) to take away one part of a group or to compare the sizes of two groups; (*noun*) the operation of taking away part of a group or comparing the difference in the sizes of two groups

sum – the answer to an addition problem

survey – to ask many people the same questions in order to gather data

symbol – a printed mark used to represent an operation or abstract idea, such as +, −, ×, ÷, <, >, =

symmetry – having the same size and shape across a dividing line

T

table – information organized in columns and rows

tenth – one of 10 equal parts in a whole; the first place to the right of the decimal point

term (of a sequence) – one of the numbers in a sequence or pattern

time interval – the amount of time that passes between two events; may be measured in seconds, minutes, hours, days, weeks, etc.

ton (T) – a customary unit equal to 2,000 pounds; used to measure weight

trapezoid – a quadrilateral with one pair of parallel sides

triangle – a polygon with three sides and three angles

two-dimensional shape – a plane figure that has length and width

U

unit fraction – a fraction with a numerator of 1, such as $\frac{1}{2}$, $\frac{1}{4}$, $\frac{1}{8}$, etc.

V

variable – a letter or symbol used to represent a number

variable expense – a cost that may change from month to month and that can be easily adjusted to balance a budget, such as the amount of money spent for restaurant meals or movie tickets

vertex/vertices – the point where two rays meet, where two sides of a polygon meet, or where the edges of a 3-dimensional figure meet; the top point of a cone or pyramid

W

weight – the measure of how heavy or light something is; measured in units such as ounces, pounds, or tons

whole – a shape or a set that is complete with no parts missing

whole number – the set of counting numbers and zero (0, 1, 2, 3, 4, ...)

width – the measure or distance across something from one side to the other

withdrawal – money removed from a savings or checking account

Y

yard (yd) – a customary unit equal to 3 feet or 36 inches; used to measure length or distance

motivation**math**™LEVEL 4